HEINEMANN GNVQ

INTERMEDIATE

Health and Social Care

Editor: Neil Moonie
Kip Chan Pensley
Beryl Stretch
Caroline Price

Heinemann Educational Publishers,
Halley Court, Jordan Hill, Oxford OX2 8EJ
A division of Reed Educational & Professional Publishing Ltd

Heinemann is a registered trademark of Reed Educational & Professional Publishing Limited

OXFORD MELBOURNE AUCKLAND JOHANNESBURG BLANTYRE GABORONE
IBADAN PORTSMOUTH NH (USA) CHICAGO

First published 2000
2004 2003 2002
10 9 8 7 6 5 4

A catalogue record for this book is available from the British Library on request.

ISBN 0 435 45293 2

Cover designed by Sarah Garbett

Pages designed by Sarah Garbett

Typeset by TechType, Abingdon, Oxfordshire

Printed and bound in Great Britain by The Bath Press Ltd., Bath

Tel: 01865 888058 www.heinemann.co.uk

HEINEMANN GNVQ

INTERMEDIATE

Health and Social Care

Editor: Neil Moonie

Kip Chan Pensley

Beryl Stretch

Caroline Price

Edexcel

Success through qualifications

Contents

Acknowledgements

The author and publisher would like to thank the following individuals and organisations for permission to reproduce tables, photographs and other material:

Gareth Boden – page 29
ChildLine – pages 17, 166
Corbis – cover
Sally & Richard Greenhill – pages 20, 32
The Stock Market – pages 23 (bottom right), 34 (bottom left), 104
The Stock Market/Zefa – page 26
Stone – pages 23 (top left), 34 (bottom right), 60, 69, 100, 103, 111.

Every effort has been made to contact copyright holders of material published in this book. We would be glad to hear from unacknowledged sources at the first opportunity.

How to use this book

This book has been written as a brand new text for students who are working to the 2000 national standards for Intermediate GNVQ in Health and Social Care. It covers the three compulsory units for the award.

The book is very different from earlier editions. In the 2000 GNVQ standards, students are assessed by one piece of work for a whole unit. The book reflects this structure. It is organised into three chapters which match exactly the three **compulsory units** at Intermediate level. These units are:

1   Health, social care and early years provision

2   Promoting health and well-being

3   Understanding personal development.

Within each chapter, the text is organised under exactly the same headings as the GNVQ units, to make it easy for you to find your way round the unit. By working through the chapters, you will find all the knowledge and ideas you need to prepare your assessment.

Assessment

Assessment in the new GNVQ is carried out on the whole unit, rather than by many smaller pieces of work. The methods of assessment are:

◊   one major assignment, for example, carrying out an investigation into the health and care provision in your local area

◊   an external test, set and marked by the awarding body, for example, Edexcel.

At the end of each chapter in the book, you will find a **Unit Assessment** section which provides you with practice for both these forms of assessment. The first part is a series of carefully planned tasks or ideas for assignments that can count towards your award. By working through the tasks you will have an opportunity to cover everything you need to obtain a *Pass* grade. Further sections then guide you towards

obtaining *Merit* and *Distinction* grades. The second part is a short unit **Test**. This can be used to check your knowledge of the chapter and also to prepare for the external test.

Special features of the book

Throughout the text there are a number of features which are designed to encourage discussion and group work, and to help you relate the theory to real work in health and social care. These activities will also help you to build up a portfolio of **key skills** by practising **numeracy**, **communication** and **ICT**. These features are:

Think it over:

Thought-provoking questions or dilemmas about people in health and social care. They can be used for individual reflection or group discussion.

Did you know?:

Interesting facts and snippets of information about the health and social care sectors.

Try it out:

Activities that encourage you to apply the theory in a practical situation.

Talk it over:

Opportunities for you to discuss your own experience with others.

Case studies: Examples of real (or simulated) clients in health and social care with real needs. Questions on the case studies will enable you to explore the key issues and deepen your understanding of the subject.

Other features, included at the end of the book, are: **Fast facts** – a glossary of key terms; **Suggestions for further reading** – including website addresses; and an **Index**. You can use these reference sections to develop your research skills.

Related titles for Intermediate GNVQ in Health and Social Care:

Student Book with Edexcel Options (0435 45600 8)

This Unit covers the knowledge you will need in order to meet the assessment requirements for Unit 1. It is written in five sections:

Section one explains the organisation of health, social care and early years services. Section two describes the main jobs in health, social care and early years. Section three explores the effective communication skills needed to support others. Section four examines the care value base. Finally section five looks at how codes of practice and charters may influence the delivery of care services.

Advice and ideas for meeting the assessment requirements for the unit and for achieving Merit and Distinction grades are at the end of the unit. Also at the end of the unit is a quick test to check your understanding.

The organisation of health, social care and early years services

This section looks at how health and social care services for adults and children are organised. Care services may be provided in one of three ways (Figure 1.1):

- **Statutory services** have been set up because Parliament has passed a law which requires the services to be provided, for example, accident and emergency departments in hospitals, education services for children or home care services for older people.

- **Private organisations** are run on a profit-making basis and are businesses, for example, private hospitals and residential homes or private children's nurseries.

- **Voluntary organisations** are run on a non-profit making basis, for example, the Woman's Royal Voluntary Services (WRVS), or Barnardo's, an organisation which provides care for children and young people.

However, health and social care is also often provided by people outside these formal agencies and organisations. **Informal care** may be provided by family members, friends and neighbours (see Figure 1.2).

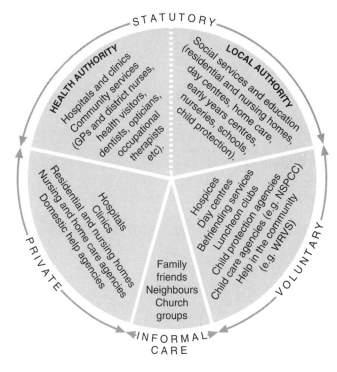

Figure 1.1 An overview of health and social care provision

Statutory sector organisations

The two main providers of statutory services are the National Health Service (**NHS**) and Local Authority services. Statutory services are organised at national, regional and local levels.

Figure 1.2   The providers of health and social care

National levels of organisation may include key government departments and the Local Government Association. Regional levels include regional services with the NHS, Health and Social Services Boards and special Health Authorities. Local levels include Local Authority social services departments, hospital and community trusts, and GPs (see Figure 1.3).

The government is divided into various departments which have responsibility for specific issues – e.g. the Department of Agriculture, Fisheries and Food; the Department of Foreign and Commonwealth Affairs; and the Department of Defence. The departments concerned with health and social care are the Department of Health, the Department of Social Security (which deals with welfare benefits) and

the Department for Education and Employment. The Home Office has responsibility for overseeing voluntary organisations. There are also specific departments that deal with issues concerning Wales, Scotland and Northern Ireland: the Welsh Office, the Scottish Office and The Northern Ireland Office (see Figure 1.4).

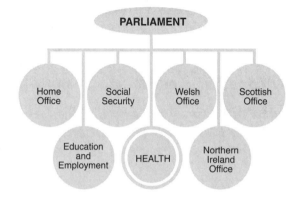

Figure 1.4   Departments of state involved in the provision of health and social care

The Secretary of State for Health in England and the Secretaries of State in Northern Ireland, Scotland and Wales are responsible for all aspects of health and social care provision. The Department of Health (**DOH**) in England has responsibility for:

◦   making policies in relation to health and social care and issuing guidelines

National

Parliament
Secretary of State for Health
Department of Health
National voluntary organisations'
headquarters

Regional

NHS, Executive regional offices
Health Authorities

Voluntary organisations' regional offices
Regional offices of private health and
social care agencies

Local

NHS trusts
Primary care groups

Local voluntary organisations
Voluntary organisations' local offices
Private health and social care agencies
Informal carers

Local authorities
social services departments

Figure 1.3   National, regional and local levels of health and social care provision

- monitoring the performance of Health Authorities and social services departments

- allocating resources for the provision of health and social care.

The Scottish Home and Health Department, the Welsh Office and the Department of Health and Social Services in Northern Ireland have similar responsibilities to those of the DOH in England. In Northern Ireland health services and social services are organised as a single agency. This is called a **unified structure** and is outside political control. Four Health Boards provide services at local levels. Although the organisation of health services in Scotland, Wales and Northern Ireland may be different from that in England, the range

and provision of services are much the same (see Figure 1.5).

The Department of Health in England and, within it, the NHS Executive, have the responsibility for deciding what plans need to be made at a national level. There are eight regional offices of the NHS Management Executive in England. These regional offices have a role in monitoring the providers of services in strategic planning. They will be responsible directly to the NHS Chief Executive (see Figure 1.6).

The structure of health services

Before 1948 health services were provided in various ways: some by voluntary organisations,

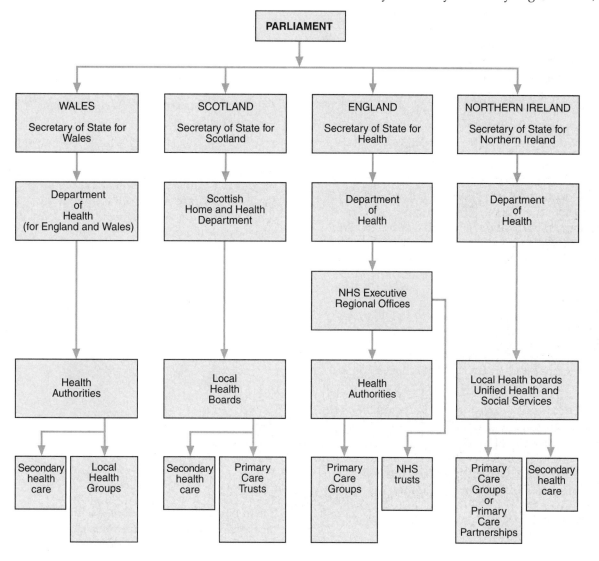

Figure 1.5   The health care structures of England, Wales, Scotland and Northern Ireland

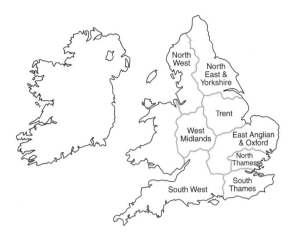

Figure 1.6   The NHS Management Executive: the English regional areas

some by Local Authorities, some by the employers of groups of people, some by private care. There was no co-ordination of services and there were inevitable gaps. Generally people had to pay for their health care. Many poor people were therefore unable to access health care when they needed it. Therefore the NHS came into being in July 1948.

The National Health Service (NHS)

The aim of the National Health Service (NHS) was to provide integrated and co-ordinated health care services to all that were free of charge at the time of use. There were three main parts to the service:

1   **Primary care** services, which include GPs, dentists, opticians and pharmacists.

2   **Secondary and tertiary care** services of the regional and district systems, for example, hospitals and specialist services

3   **Community care** and **public health services**, which had an emphasis on preventative work and health promotion. Early examples of these included vaccination and immunisation programmes against illnesses such as smallpox and whooping cough.

Find out from your local Health Authority about any preventative health care programmes that are being carried out in your area.

Until recently there were only comparatively minor changes in the way the NHS was structured. However the NHS has now undergone major reforms that have been more far-reaching than any other changes undertaken since it was set up in 1948.

These reforms are set out in four government **White Papers**:

1   *Promoting better health* (1987), which concerns primary health care

2   *Working for patients* (1989), which discusses the management and provision of services.

3   *Caring for people* (1989), concerning community care

4   *The New NHS* (1998), which sets out the future of the NHS.

In addition to these White Papers, the **NHS and Community Care Act 1990** had important consequences for the way health and social care agencies are organised. At the centre of the reforms to health and social care was the idea there should be a clear division between purchasing and the provision of services. The idea of **purchasers** and

Stella is comparing estimates which she has received from catering firms to do the catering at her sister's 18th birthday party – she is acting as a *purchaser* of a service and the catering firm she chooses will be the *provider* of the service.

providers might best be understood by thinking about obtaining estimates for the catering at a wedding reception or some other large social event. You decide it would be too difficult or expensive to provide the catering yourself, so you contact a number of catering firms to supply you with estimates. Once you have studied the estimates you decide which firm provides the best value for money. You contact this firm again and go ahead to book them to supply the catering. In this situation, you are the **purchaser** of the services. The catering firm you have chosen is the **provider** of the services, and you have chosen your provider by comparing the services offered by others in the same market. NHS and social services departments were therefore split into those departments who have the responsibility for 'buying' services (the purchasers – deciding how the NHS budget should be spent and deciding on the allocation of funds for the provision of different services) and those departments which decide who should provide these services, eg hospitals, dentists and district nurses. In the health service the old District Health Authorities became the purchasers, together with some GP group practices, which became **GP fundholders**. In social services departments, it was the senior managers who became the purchasers. Residential homes, day centres and home care units became the providers.

Health Authorities

Before April 1996 the structure of the administration and provision of health care services within the NHS was quite complicated. This structure included 8 Regional Health Authorities in England (and 3 separate ones in Wales, Scotland and Northern Ireland) 90 Family Health Service Authorities and 186 District Health Authorities (see Figure 1.7).

In April 1996 the Regional Health Authorities were abolished and the District Health Authorities and Family Service Authorities were combined to form 100 new Health Authorities (**HAs**). The Health Authorities are now the main purchasers of care. Each Health Authority has a population of between 125,000 and one million people. The responsibilities of the new Health Authorities reflect on those previously held by the District Health Authorities and Family Health Service Authorities. These include:

- planning services in the Health Authority's area (with national guidelines)
- assessing primary health care needs
- developing services within the area
- **commissioning** (i.e. requesting others to provide, for a fee) primary care

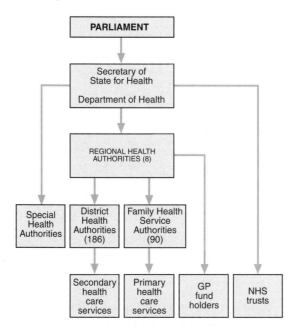

Figure 1.7   The structure of the NHS in England before April 1996

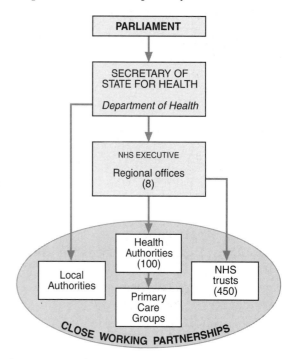

Figure 1.8   The structure of the NHS in England after April 1999

- arranging contracts with acute services, such as hospitals
- managing services provided by GPs, dentists, opticians and pharmacists
- monitoring the quality of services
- providing information to the public about services
- registering and dealing with complaints about the provision of services.

It is expected that, in the future, the Health Authorities will work closely with Primary Care Groups (**PCGs**), **NHS trusts** and Local Authorities (see Figure 1.8).

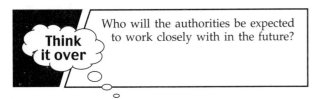

Think it over

Who will the authorities be expected to work closely with in the future?

NHS trusts

National Health trusts are self-governing units within the health service. Trusts are run by a board of directors and are accountable to central government. There are now 450 trusts in England. A trust can either be a hospital, a group of hospitals, community services (such as district nursing) or ambulance services for a particular area.

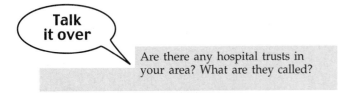

Talk it over

Are there any hospital trusts in your area? What are they called?

A trust is able to:

- decide its own management structure
- employ staff under its own terms and conditions of employment, including salary scales
- buy, own and sell assets, such as land or buildings
- keep surplus money or borrow money
- carry out research
- provide facilities for medical education and other forms of training.

Self-governing trusts receive most of their income from NHS contracts for providing services to Health Authorities and Primary Care Groups. However, they can also treat private patients. All trusts must write annual reports and maintain annual accounts, and they must publish these. This means they are now more accountable to the public in the way they spend their money – and most of their money came from the public in the first place!

Primary care groups

From April 1999 Primary Care Groups (made up of groups of GPs and community nurses) took responsibility for commissioning services within their area. They also now work closely with social services departments. In England each group services about 100,000 patients and may have about 50 GPs, but this varies according to local circumstances. PCGs have replaced the former GP fundholding system that was introduced in the 1980s.

PCGs may do all or any of the following tasks (see Figure 1.9), although the majority of PCGs will initially operate at Level 2.

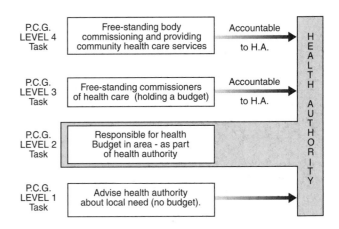

Figure 1.9   Primary Care Groups: levels of responsibility

- Become a free-standing body for providing community care services – again accountable to the HA.
- Become a free-standing body for commissioning health care – accountable to the HA.
- Take responsibility for managing the health budget in its area – as part of the HA.

◦ Advise the health authority (HA) about needs of the local community.

In addition they are responsible for:

◦ contributing to and implementing the government's Health Improvement Programme

◦ promoting the health of the local population

◦ developing primary care services in their areas

◦ integrating primary and community health services

◦ being involved in the development and monitoring of the quality of services.

This is the situation in England. In Scotland, primary care trusts oversee the delivery of services, and GPs are responsible only for primary care budgets. Wales has local health groups (equivalent to PCGs) but these have only an advisory role. At the time of writing it has yet to be decided whether Northern Ireland will have PCGs or primary care partnerships.

Provision of health care

The provision of health services is divided into these following areas:

1 **Primary care** is usually the first contact a person has with the health services and this is often provided in the community (GPs, dentists, opticians, etc.). Primary care is often preventative in nature (e.g. routine dental check-ups and eye tests).

2 **Secondary care** usually follows referral from a primary care worker (e.g. a GP may refer a patient to a hospital for tests and specialist investigations) Secondary care is often curative in nature (e.g. operations, setting broken bones, removing wisdom teeth etc.) and is given in hospitals, day surgeries and out-patient clinics.

Some services function as both primary and secondary care. A paramedic giving treatment at the scene of an accident is an example of primary care; a paramedic working in the ambulance service collecting a patient for treatment at a hospital is an example of secondary care.

3 **Tertiary care** may be provided by specialist units which are able to give longer-term, rehabilitative treatment – for example, a unit providing intensive physiotherapy following an accident where a patient suffered spinal injuries.

4 **Community services** provide care for people within the community, often in their own homes. Examples include district nurses, health visitors and chiropodists.

5 **Public health services** include health education and programmes and schemes to prevent illnesses and disease. Both the health services and Local Authorities have various roles in the promotion of better health.

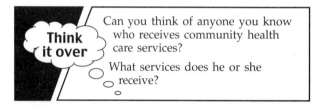

Think it over

Can you think of anyone you know who receives community health care services?

What services does he or she receive?

Talk it over

What is the difference between primary and secondary care?

The structure of the social services

The introduction of the National Health Service in 1948 also meant a range of health and social care services came under the direct control of the Minister of Health. It was hoped this direct control would result in a more unified and co-ordinated range of services. The responsibility for providing for old and disabled people and children by the Local Authorities was extended further. Also, services for people with mental health problems were strengthened through the setting up of the Provisional Council for Mental Health. However, until the 1960s these three areas of care were operated quite separately from one another. The publication of the **Seebohm Report**, in 1968, resulted in the amalgamation of the children's departments and the welfare services. Then, in 1970, the Local Authority Social Services Act set out a new framework for social care provision, which required the Local Authorities to set up Social Services Committees (see Figure 1.10).

Parliament

↓

Secretary of State for Health

↓

Department of Health

↓

Local Authorities

↓

Social Services Committees

↓

Social Services Departments

Figure 1.10   The structure of social care in England

Although the Secretary of State is responsible for the provision of social care, it is the Local Authorities who administer those services. In England and Wales, county councils, metropolitan councils and the London boroughs run the Local Authorities. In Northern Ireland there are four boards who administer the combined health and social services. In Scotland regional Local Authorities control social services departments.

However, the powers and responsibilities of Local Authorities are defined by parliament, which passes legislation outlining the Local Authorities' duties.

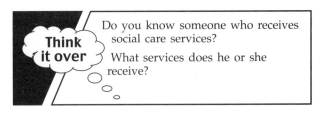

Think it over

Do you know someone who receives social care services?

What services does he or she receive?

Local Authorities have the responsibility for the co-ordination of many aspects of social care in their communities, including services for children, for people with physical disabilities, people with learning disabilities and people with mental health problems, as well as responsibilities for housing, education, leisure facilities, refuse collection and highways.

Each Local Authority must appoint a Director of Social Services and must have a Social Services Committee. Some Local Authorities have separate directorates for each of their responsibilities (e.g. social services, housing, education, etc.). Others combine these departments at senior management level (e.g. housing with community care for adults – i.e. services for the elderly, people with

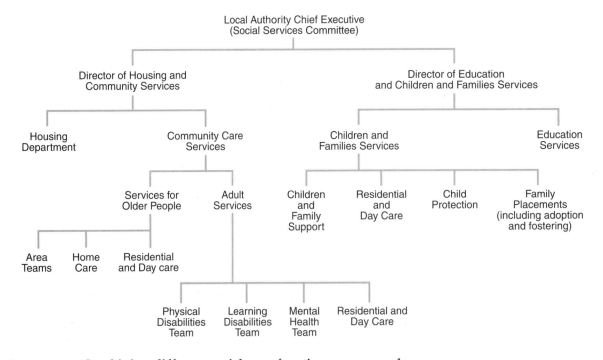

Figure 1.11   Combining different social care functions: an example

disabilities, people with health problems – and children and families with education) (see Figure 1.11).

The organisational structures of social services departments have changed considerably in the past few years. This has happened so that they can carry out their new roles and responsibilities as required by new legislation, particularly the NHS and Community Care Act 1990. As mentioned earlier, this Act made Local Authorities the purchasers of care, rather than the providers of care. Many social services departments reorganised their staffing structures to reflect these changes in responsibilities (see Figure 1.12).

The role of social service departments

The role of the social service departments has changed as their function as direct providers of services has decreased and their role as assessors of need and purchasers of services has increased. Their main role now is to offer advice and to provide access to services, such as residential care, for all client groups (e.g. children, people with physical or learning disabilities, people with mental health problems or older people). Previously, Local Authorities owned and managed a number of residential homes themselves. Today they are more likely to purchase residential care

for individuals in private or non-profit-making residential homes.

Talk it over

Make a list of the 'client groups' who receive services from social services departments.

Social workers are employed within the social services departments, and their role is to assess the needs of people requiring social care services. Social workers are often organised into teams that deal with a specific client group (e.g. children and families teams, teams for older people). Sometimes, teams consist of health and social care workers (for example, teams dealing with people with mental health problems may work side by side with social workers and community psychiatric nurses).

With their increased role in the purchasing of services, many social services departments have created special commissioning and **contracting** sections. (Contracting means employing someone who does not regularly work for your organisation to do a specific job for you – for

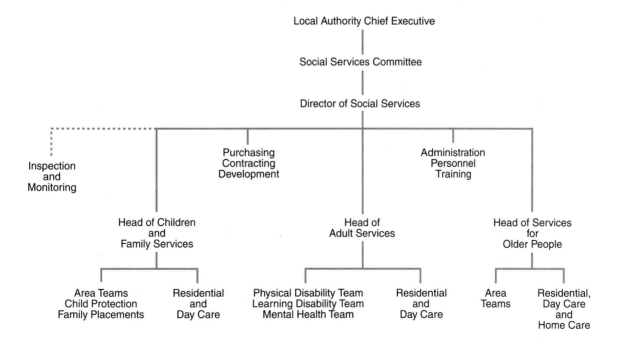

Figure 1.12   A Local Authority's social services department

example, employing cleaners through an agency). These new sections operate alongside divisions created as a result of the 1990 Act (e.g. complaints, inspection and registration units, quality monitoring and planning and development). Planning and development has become even more important as social services departments are required to work closely with health service colleagues, as well as with the private and voluntary sectors.

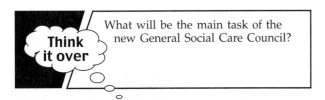

Talk it over

How could you find out if there are any services in your area where health and social services staff work together in teams to provide care?

The government has plans for modernising social services departments. These plans are set out in the white paper *Modernising Social Services*. Changes include new independent inspection units for care homes and other services and better support for adults – including the introduction of direct payment schemes to clients. Clients will then be able to spend their allowance on care providers of their own choice. There will also be Quality Projects to ensure children are properly protected against abuse; to raise standards of care in children's homes; and to give children better opportunities to receive a good education. Additionally, a new General Social Care Council will be formed. Its function will be to raise the standards of care given by social care staff. To achieve this there will be more emphasis on staff training and on monitoring the services provided.

Think it over

What will be the main task of the new General Social Care Council?

Joint work and planning

Health and social services must now work together to modernise the front-line care they provide for people. In September 1998, the targets set for achieving this were outlined in *Modernising Health and Social Services: National Priorities*

Guidance 1999–2002. The priorities contained in this document included the following:

- Cutting waiting lists and waiting times.

- Modernising mental health and primary care services.

- Reducing deaths from cancer and coronary heart disease, and improving the health of the most disadvantaged in society.

- Improving the quality and safety of children's services and providing better rehabilitation services for older people.

Think it over

There have been a lot of newspaper articles in recent times about the length of time people are on hospital waiting lists and are waiting for operations.

Do you think hospital waiting times are getting shorter?

Ask a few people their opinions.

Previous governments tried to encourage joint planning between the health and Local Authorities. However, this was difficult to achieve because of the different ways the authorities were structured. For example, in terms of health, the care of the elderly, mentally ill people was the responsibility of the mental health services, whereas, in terms of social care, the same people came under the remit of services for older people.

Other problems have arisen because Health Authorities and Local Authorities do not share the same geographical boundaries. For example,

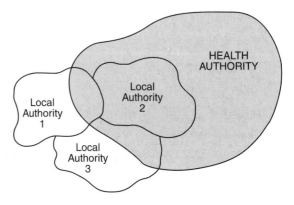

Figure 1.13   A Health Authority that covers more than one Local Authority area

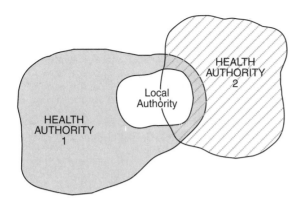

Figure 1.14 A Local Authority that comes under the control of more than one Health Authority

one Health Authority may cover all or part of a Local Authority's area (see Figure 1.13) or one Local Authority's area may come under the responsibility of a number of Health Authorities (see Figure 1.14).

Early years services

Structure
The early years services are those services that provide health, care and education services to children between the ages of 0 and 8, when not at school. As with the health and social services, the early years services involve both the statutory sector and voluntary and private groups

Statutory services
The government's role is to provide statutory services directly, or to supervise services through government departments. The four main government departments concerned with children are shown in Figure 1.15. Funding from these central government departments is passed on to

Local Authorities in the form of grants. The authorities then use these grants to provide services for children and families in their areas. The three main services are health, education and social services.

Health services for children
In addition to the health care offered to all, there are special services for children:

1 *Health screening* From the age of 10 weeks, all children are seen in their own homes by health visitors, who give children regular developmental tests. These tests are for growth and development, sight and hearing.

2 *Vaccinations and immunisations* Children are given a programme of injections starting at the age of 8 weeks to protect them from whooping cough, polio, tetanus, measles and other infectious diseases.

3 *School health services* Once they start school, children are seen by a school nurse and given health education.

4 *Dental services* Dental check-ups and orthodontic treatment (straightening the teeth) are free to children up to the age of 16 years.

5 *Maternity services* Before a baby is born and up to 10 weeks after the birth, the mother and child are looked after by a midwife.

6 *Community and hospital services* If children need referral for specialist treatment, they may see a paediatrician (a doctor who treats sick children), audiologist, speech therapist, optician or dietician.

All these services are free to children under the age of 16 years.

Figure 1.15 Government departments concerned with children

Department	Responsible for
1 Department of Health (DOH)	Health services, including hospitals and local health care
2 Department for Education and Employment (DfEE)	All aspects of education and employment, including standards in schools and day nurseries
3 Department of Social Security (DSS)	Providing benefits for children and families
4 Department of the Environment, Transport and the Regions (DETR)	Local government, housing, planning and the countryside

Talk it over

Jake is $3^{1}/_{2}$ years old. He is small for his age and doesn't want to eat.

Which health services might Jake's family make use of?

Talk it over

The Rajiahs have two children aged 1 and 4 years. Both parents work full time and have well paid jobs. Their current nanny is leaving them after three years and they feel Manzoor, the 4-year-old, might be ready for a nursery or playgroup.

What care might suit the Rajiahs – a nanny, a day nursery or both? Discuss this in groups and give reasons for your recommendation.

Education for children

Local Education Authorities are responsible for delivering nursery, primary and secondary education in their areas. Children are required to be in full-time education in the school term following their fifth birthday. However, many children start a year earlier (the 'reception year').

By law every 4-year-old is entitled to receive some nursery education. This may take place in private day nurseries or playgroups. Any nursery wanting to receive government funding for 4-year-olds must be inspected by Ofsted, the school inspection service. Nurseries must follow the Early Learning Goals, which is a special curriculum for children aged 3–5 years.

Social services for children

The Department of Social Security (**DSS**) is responsible for providing benefits for children and families, and it also runs the **Child Support Agency**. A number of benefits are available for children and families, and the main ones are as follows:

- *Child Benefit* A fixed payment to all parents who have a child or children.
- *Maternity Benefit* Money paid to working mothers while they are on leave from work to have a baby.
- *Family Credit* Payments for families with a child or children where the family's income is low.

The benefits system is complex and changes frequently.

Local Authorities are responsible for a range of services, particularly for registering people who work with children in early years settings. These settings may be statutory, private or voluntary (see Figure 1.16).

The National Childcare Strategy

The government has recently made a decision to focus on the early years to ensure that preschool children are provided with good-quality care and education. There have been a number of key developments:

- A national framework of qualifications for people who work with children to ensure everyone understands the levels and achievements attained through the various training courses currently on offer.
- The preschool curriculum entitled 'Early Learning Goals'.
- Inspection by Ofsted of all preschool settings to ensure they are following a balanced programme of learning and play.
- Early Years Development Partnerships, where all Local Authorities have to produce a plan to show how the local health, social care and education services are working together for children.

Early Years Development Partnership and Plans

These plans are seen as the key to ensuring there is good quality local provision for all children. Some of the key aims of the plans are to:

- make sure every 4-year-old has three terms of good quality preschool education
- include children with special needs within the same care and education settings as other children
- show how the provisions of the Children Act 1989 and other laws relating to children are being fulfilled

Figure 1.16 Child care settings

Setting	Sector	Description
Childminders	Private; registered with Local Authority	A childminder looks after other people's children in the childminder's own home. This might include looking after other children after school as well as looking after children under 5 years of age during the day
Nannies	Private; no registration required	A nanny looks after children in the children's own home
Day nurseries	Statutory or private; inspected by Ofsted	A day nursery is open all year round and children under 5 years of age can stay all day
Workplace nurseries	Statutory or private; inspected by Ofsted	A workplace nursery is organised by an employer and the places are often subsidised. This means the employee does not pay the full cost
Crèches	Private or Local Authority run	Crèches look after children under 8 years of age for short periods of time. For example, they are found in new shopping centres, allowing parents to shop for a few hours
Playgroups	Voluntary or private	Playgroups are non-profit making groups designed to give children under 5 years of age an opportunity to play. Sessions are often two to three hours long
Nurseries or kindergartens	Statutory or private; inspected by Ofsted	Nurseries and kindergartens offer sessions in mornings and afternoons that allow children under 5 years of age to learn and play
Nurseries within schools	Run by Local Education Authority	Some infant or primary schools have a nursery attached. The nurseries take children from 3 to 4 years of age. No charge is made to the parents
Infant and primary schools	Run by Local Education Authority; inspected by Ofsted	Infant and primary schools take children from the age of 5 years. The normal school day is about six hours long
After-school clubs	Can be voluntary or private	After-school clubs look after children over the age of 5 years after school has finished during term time. They are often used by working parents
Holiday play schemes	Run by Local Authorities, and private and voluntary groups	Holiday play schemes look after children over the age of 5 years during school holidays. They are often used by working parents

- promote training for all early years workers (for example, NVQs in early years care)
- provide grants for training.

For example, a childminder might decide she would like to be NVQ trained so that she is better equipped to help the children she looks after. She could apply for a grant from her Local Authority to help her with her training to achieve this.

CASE STUDY – Michelle and her children

Michelle is a single mum with two children, Jade aged $4^1/_2$ years and Kai aged 2 years. She is living with her own mother at the moment, but wants to find her own home and to obtain a part-time job to help her support the children. Both the children are at home at present, but Jade is due to start school in 3 months. Michelle is anxious that Jade won't find it easy to be separated from her. Kai worries her too, because he is asthmatic and has had two recent serious asthma attacks. Michelle needs to find good-quality care and health support for him. Then there is the problem of finding a job. Michelle wants something that will fit in with her plans for the children and will pay enough to cover her child care costs. Her mum can help for a few hours a week, but no more.

Questions

1   What early years services will Michelle need for herself and her children? You could note them down under the headings: 'Health', 'Education' and 'Social care'.

2   How could Michelle find out about these services?

3   Imagine Michelle had moved into your local area. Where would she find the services she needs?

Voluntary and private organisations

Voluntary organisations

The UK has a long tradition of voluntary services, and this sector has always been involved in the provision of health and social care. For example, in the eighteenth and nineteenth centuries private benefactors established many hospitals which provided care free of charge. In 1866, Dr Barnardo's (now known simply as Barnardo's) was established to help orphaned and underprivileged children and, in 1889, the NSPCC (National Society for the Prevention of Cruelty to Children) was founded. By the middle of the nineteenth century there were so many voluntary organisations (many of them overlapping in the services they provided), that the Charity Organisation Society (COS) was set up to help co-ordinate these various organisations.

Today, the National Council for Voluntary Organisations (NCVO) is the main co-ordinating agency in England. Its main function is to provide links between voluntary organisations, official bodies and the private sector. Councils in Scotland, Wales and Northern Ireland have similar roles. There are over 200,000 voluntary organisations in the UK, and more than 170,000 of these are registered as charities. Throughout the UK, the Home Office is the government department with responsibility for co-ordinating government interests in the voluntary sector (see Figure 1.17).

Figure 1.17   The structure of voluntary organisations in England

There are thousands of voluntary organisations involved in health and social care, ranging from national agencies (such as Age Concern) to local small groups. In recent years **self-help groups** have greatly increased in number. Self-help groups are usually set up by people who share a particular concern and who want to help other people in similar situations. For example, Compassionate Friends was set up to help the brothers and sisters of children who have died. Groups representing women's interests (e.g. the

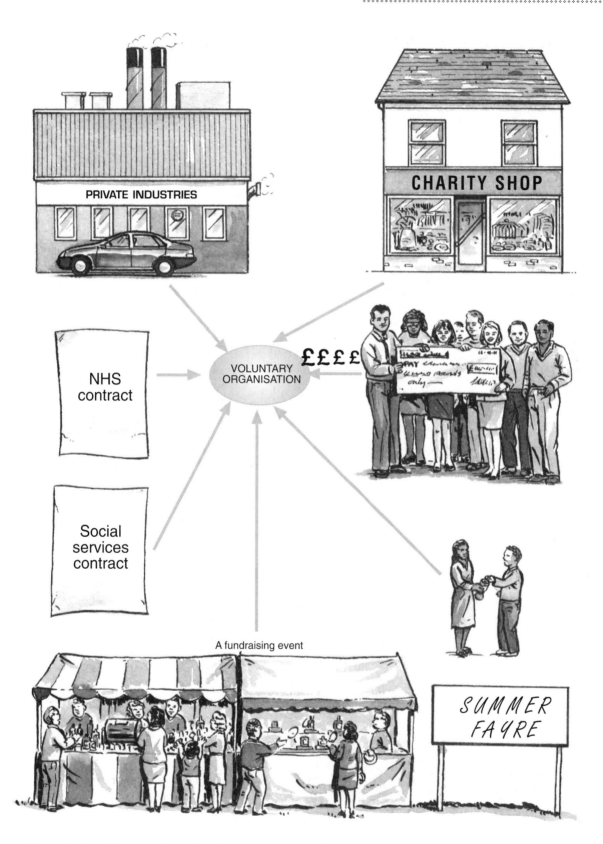

Figure 1.18   The funding of voluntary organisations

Irish Women's Housing Action Group) and ethnic minority groups (e.g. the Cantonese Healthline) have also increased in number recently.

Funding for voluntary organisations comes from various sources. Some have contracts with Health Authorities or Local Authorities, who provide services for them. For example, some hospices (who provide specialist care for people with terminal illnesses) have contracts with Health Authorities and Local Authorities have contracts with local branches of Age Concern, through which they provide luncheon clubs for the more able older people in their areas. Other funds are obtained through fund-raising events, through charitable donations from individuals or groups of people, and through grants from grant-awarding bodies. Some larger companies donate money to charities for specific purposes (see Figure 1.18).

Voluntary organisations tend to focus on specific issues (see Figure 1.19).

Some examples of health, social care and early years voluntary agencies are given below.

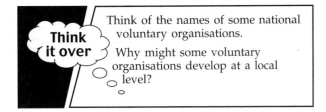

Think it over

Think of the names of some national voluntary organisations.

Why might some voluntary organisations develop at a local level?

Health: John Groomes Association for the Disabled

This charitable organisation was set up in 1866. It provides residential accommodation for people with severe disabilities, sheltered work and specialist housing throughout England and Wales. The association also provides holidays and short breaks for people with disabilities, their families and friends. It runs an information service about the problems and needs of people with disabilities.

Social care: Age Concern

Age Concern is a registered charity, which depends largely on public support for the financing of its activities. Although Age Concern provides services throughout the UK, it is divided into four regions: England, Scotland, Wales and Ireland. There is a network of over 1,400 local groups, with the support of around 250,000 volunteers plus some paid staff. The aim of Age Concern is to improve the quality of life for older people and to develop services appropriate to local needs. These services may include advice and information, day care, visiting services, transport schemes, clubs and specialist facilities for older people who have physical disabilities or who are mentally frail.

Early years: National Society for the Prevention of Cruelty to Children

The National Society for the Prevention of Cruelty to Children (NSPCC) was set up to protect

Figure 1.19 Voluntary organisations and their principal areas of concern

Area of concern	Organisation
Personal and family problems	Family Welfare Association; Child Poverty Action Group; Relate (formerly Marriage Guidance); Barnardo's; ChildLine; National Council for One-Parent Families; National Society for the Prevention of Cruelty to Children; Claimants' Union (advice on social security benefits); Samaritans (for lonely, depressed and suicidal people); Women's Aid
Health and disability	WRVS (Women's Royal Voluntary Service); MIND (National Association for Mental Health); Gamanon (for people with gambling problems); Help the Aged; Brook Advisory Centres; Institute for the Blind; National Institute for Deaf People; Alcoholics Anonymous; British Red Cross Society; Haemophilia Society
National organisations whose work is religious in inspiration	Salvation Army; Church Army; TocH; Church's Urban Fund; Church of England Children's Society; Young Men's Christian Association (YMCA); Catholic Marriage Advisory Council; Jewish Welfare Board

children from abuse. The organisation receives approximately 88% of its running costs from public donations. It operates throughout the UK and its workers are organised into area teams. These child protection teams assess and help abused children and their families. The work is carried out either in the family's home or in NSPPC centres. The teams also offer a 24-hour advice service and local education, training, consultation and advice for other professional and voluntary organisations.

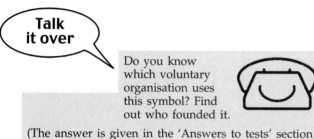

Talk it over

Do you know which voluntary organisation uses this symbol? Find out who founded it.

(The answer is given in the 'Answers to tests' section at the end of the book.)

Private health and social care organisations

The work of private organisations in the provision of health and social care has always been important. These organisations charge for their services with the intention of making a profit (i.e. they are run as businesses). Some of the services provided by the private sector are shown in Figure 1.20.

Figure 1.20   Health and social care services provided by the private sector

The range and extent of services available from private organisations have increased considerably in recent years. In particular, there was a rapid growth in private health care in the 1970s and 1980s when central government introduced the

> *Today, over three million people subscribe to private health care insurance schemes.*

idea of a **mixed economy of care**. It is now government policy that NHS and private and voluntary health care provision should co-operate in meeting the nation's health needs. Private health care may be provided by NHS hospital trusts or in totally separate health care facilities. Similarly, the government expects Local Authorities to use private and voluntary agencies to provide them with social care, rather than own and manage these services themselves. Consequently, a number of small businesses have emerged in recent years, for example, ironing services, home-help services and private health clinics.

Services for older people

Local Authorities have the **duty** to assess the needs of older people and the power to provide services in order to meet those needs. However, they do not have to provide services themselves. For example, an older person may need assistance in getting up and washed each morning but this 'home care' service may be provided either by people employed directly by the authority or by people employed by a private agency. In the latter case, the Local Authority may have a contract with the agency to provide home care for such people. The range of services provided by a Local Authority can include:

- personal care (e.g. getting up, getting washed, dressing, going to bed and bathing)
- meals and light refreshments
- domestic help (e.g. shopping, housework, laundry and pension collecting)
- equipment (e.g. stair lifts and bath aids)
- personal alarm systems
- adaptations to the home (e.g. ramps, widening doorways, downstairs toilet)
- day care facilities
- residential homes
- nursing homes (although these may be funded by the health service).

Health Authorities also have a duty to assist older people who live at home. Community Health Services employ, for example, district nurses, occupational therapists, speech therapists, continence advisers, and chiropodists, etc., to provide these services. The help that may be offered includes:

- nursing care at home
- personal care – especially if the person has a terminal illness
- equipment (e.g. bath seats, hand-rails, walking frames, wheelchairs, commodes)
- aids to dressing, eating and carrying out everyday tasks

CASE STUDY – Mrs Low Ying

Mrs Low Ying is an 80-year-old Chinese lady. She was widowed seven years ago and lives alone in a two-bedroomed house. None of her family live nearby and Mrs Low Ying is very isolated and often lonely. About a month ago Mrs Low Ying's arthritis, which she has in her hands, legs and feet, became very bad and her mobility was greatly reduced. She also has angina and high blood pressure. Following a joint assessment visit by a district nurse and a social worker the following services were provided.

Local Authority

1   Every morning a home carer helps Mrs Low Ying with getting up, washing and dressing (the Local Authority has a contract with a private agency for home care services). In the evenings she can still manage to get herself back to bed.

2   Once a week the Local Authority provides help with her shopping, with the collection of her pension and with her household tasks (also provided through the private home care agency).

3   Meals-on-wheels are provided five days a week as she can no longer prepare her own food (the WRVS prepare and deliver meals on behalf of the Local Authority).

4   A stair-lift has been installed, as she can no longer get up the stairs by herself.

5   Ramps have been fitted from the front and back doors.

6   A disabled badge has been provided for her niece's car so that her niece can take her out and park close to shops, etc.

7   A personal alarm system has been installed so that she can call for help if she should have a fall.

8   Day care is provided at a local centre one day per week (Age Concern run the centre and arrange transport for Mrs Low Ying).

Health Authority

1   A district nurse helps Mrs Low Ying to have a bath once a week and also monitors her medication.

2   A bath seat, grab-rails and a raised toilet seat have been installed.

3   She has been supplied with a walking frame for use inside the home, and a wheelchair for going out.

Informal Carer

Mrs Low Ying's niece visits each Sunday and provides a meal that day. She also does her Aunt's laundry for her.

Questions

1   Does Mrs Low Ying receive a 'mixed economy of care' package?

2   What is meant by a 'mixed economy of care?'

3   What other care needs might Mrs Low Ying have in the future? Who might provide these?

- help with continence problems, including pads, pants and other aids
- help with speech and swallowing problems
- foot care and chiropody.

Informal carers

In recent years the term **carer** has been used to describe anyone, other than a paid worker, who is looking after someone who is ill or disabled. The carer may be a family member, friend or neighbour (for example, a wife looking after a disabled partner, a parent looking after a child with learning difficulties, an adult looking after a parent who has dementia or a friend looking after someone who has a long-term illness). It could even be a child who is looking after a sick or disabled parent.

Some people do not like the term 'carer' but it does at least acknowledge that the carer is doing a 'job' of work and one which can be very difficult and demanding. Informal carers may:

- help people to get from and return to bed
- help people to wash and dress
- help people to bathe or shower
- prepare refreshments and meals
- do domestic work and shopping
- monitor and dispense medicines
- provide transport.

Informal carers may also be people who belong to a local group, such as a church, or a group set up to help and advise other carers.

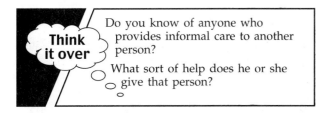

Think it over

Do you know of anyone who provides informal care to another person?

What sort of help does he or she give that person?

The main jobs in health, social care and early years services

People who work in health, social care and early years services may be involved in either **direct care** or **indirect care**. People who deliver *direct* care will meet clients face to face (for example,

occupational therapists, social workers and nursery nurses). However, there are jobs that are necessary to support those who deliver direct care but the people who perform these jobs may not come into face-to-face contact with the clients (for example, laboratory technicians, secretaries, catering staff and cleaners).

There are too many jobs in the fields of health, social care and early years services to include all of them in this book but the following pages describe a respresentative selection. You will be able to find out about the jobs not described here from careers guides (copies of these will be found in your local college or local library as well as at your local careers office).

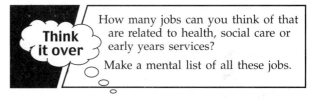

Think it over

How many jobs can you think of that are related to health, social care or early years services?

Make a mental list of all these jobs.

Jobs in the direct provision of health care

The NHS is the biggest employer of staff in Europe but not everyone who is involved in the provision of health care is employed by the NHS (see Figure 1.21). As we have already seen, some health care professionals are employed by voluntary organisations, by private companies, by government departments or are self-employed. While some health care jobs require basic training (such as nursing), others require more specialised training in addition to the basic training (such as midwifery).

Talk it over

What is the difference in the roles of a midwife and a health visitor?

You may need to talk to someone who is a midwife or health visitor to find out about this.

In the past ten years the use of **complementary therapies** (such as aromatherapy and homeopathy) has increased, and these therapies are rapidly becoming accepted and are now used alongside **conventional medicines and treatment**. This has resulted in yet a further increase in the

Figure 1.21   A few of the main jobs in health care

Doctors	Nurses	Therapists	Others	Support staff
Gynaecologist	District nurse	Physiotherapist	Chemist	Environmental health officer
Psychiatrist	Community psychiatric nurse	Aromatherapist*	Pharmacist	Administrator
Cardiologist	Ward co-ordinator or manager (sister)	Speech therapist	Chiropodist	Health service manager
Dermatologist	Health visitor	Art therapist*	Radiographer	Ambulance crew
Physician	Hospital nurse	Hypnotherapist*	Dietician	Catering officer
General practitioner	Midwife	Counsellor	Optician	Domestic supervisor
Surgeon	Nursing auxiliary	Drama therapist*	Pathologist	Laboratory technician
Geriatrician	Nurse for people with learning disabilities	Acupuncturist*	Anaesthetist	Medical records officer
Neurologist	Occupational health nurse	Homoeopath*	Dentist	Medical secretary
Paediatrician	Paediatric nurse	Osteopath*		Radiotherapist
Rheumatologist		Psychologist		Receptionist

Note: * **Complementary therapies.**

range of health care work currently available, although most complementary therapies are provided outside the NHS.

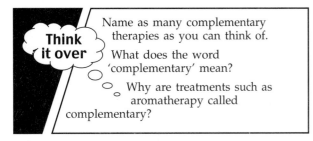

Think it over

Name as many complementary therapies as you can think of.

What does the word 'complementary' mean?

Why are treatments such as aromatherapy called complementary?

Try it out

Find out about how at least one complementary therapy works. For example, try using scented oils in your bath.

Hospital nurses

Hospital nurses are responsible for the nursing care of patients when they are in hospital. Nursing care involves such tasks as the following:

- Taking the patients' temperature, blood pressure and respiration rate.

- Giving patients injections.

- Administering medications.

- Cleaning and dressing wounds.

- Bandaging and splinting.

- Administering blood transfusions and drips.

- Routine tasks, such as bed-making, ensuring the patients are comfortable or escorting patients to other departments, such as X-ray or the operating theatre.

Nurses must familiarise themselves with the patients' medical history and circumstances; they must keep a careful record of the treatment that is given; and they must record the patients' progress. They must also take into account the patients' emotional and social needs, thus bringing a **'holistic' approach** to patient care (i.e. by addressing all these different needs, nurses provide an overall service to their patients that

A nurse on a hospital ward

means more to the patients than if nurses simply performed practical tasks).

A nurse works as part of a *team* of nurses on the wards, or in other units within the hospital, such as the accident and emergency unit or out-patient clinics. A nurse also works as part of a multi-disciplinary team, which includes doctors, occupational therapists, physiotherapists and social workers. All the members of the multi-disciplinary team come together to ensure that patients receive as much help and support as they need so they can return to the community (see Figure 1.22).

There are many different types of ward on which nurses may work, including medical, surgical, orthopaedic (the correction of deformities in a patient's skeleton) and children's. There are also various units where they may be employed, such as operating theatre, out-patient clinics, maternity care units and intensive care units. There are areas of specialist work as well, for example, working with people who have neurological problems (such as people who have epileptic fits), or people who are receiving treatment for cancer.

The type of hospital a nurse might find him or herself working in can also vary enormously.

Figure 1.22   A multi-disciplinary team

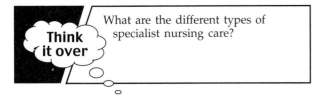

What are the different types of specialist nursing care?

Some are very large and have a number of specialised wards and departments, out-patient clinics, an accident and emergency unit and operating theatres. Others may be much smaller and may specialise (for example in care for the elderly, for people with mental health problems or in health care specifically for children).

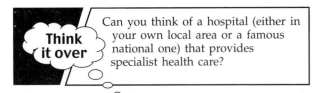

Can you think of a hospital (either in your own local area or a famous national one) that provides specialist health care?

From the beginning of their training, nurses may choose to specialise in one form of nursing (see Figure 1.23). Nurses undertaking adult and general nursing training will spend time on many different wards and units during their training, but may still specialise in specific aspects of nursing.

Figure 1.23   The specialised divisions of nursing

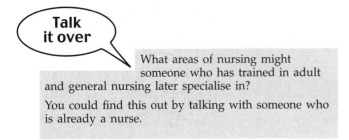

What areas of nursing might someone who has trained in adult and general nursing later specialise in?

You could find this out by talking with someone who is already a nurse.

Skills and qualities

Nursing is physically, intellectually and emotionally demanding work. Trainee nurses are required to take in large quantities of knowledge, and the work itself can be very physically draining, as much time is spent walking from one location to another and can involve the trainees helping the patients move about the hospital. Being faced with illness or injury is always traumatic for both patients and their relatives, and the nurse will often be required to talk with patients about their situation, their problems and their fears, as well as having to deal with their worried relatives. Nurses need to be able to deal with difficult situations and distressed patients and families. They must remain calm and caring and must not become distressed themselves. They also need to be observant: they have to take in a lot of information and make sense of it. They must also be able to communicate clearly, both verbally and in writing.

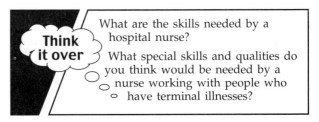

What are the skills needed by a hospital nurse?

What special skills and qualities do you think would be needed by a nurse working with people who have terminal illnesses?

Nurses often have to work shifts, sometimes starting work early in the morning and finishing late in the evening. They may also be required to work at night, at weekends and on bank holidays. They therefore need to be adaptable in their working patterns (see Figure 1.24).

Figure 1.24   The skills and qualities required of a hospital nurse

General practitioners (GPs)

The GP, or family doctor, is very important in the provision of primary health care. The GP is often the first person to be consulted when someone is feeling unwell. It is the job of the GP to make any necessary examinations and, where possible, to make a diagnosis of the problem or illness and to prescribe appropriate medicines. GPs are now also increasingly performing minor operations.

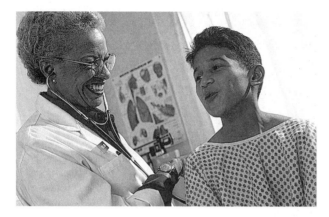

A general practitioner

GPs will advise people on how to manage an illness, disability or problem. They often become concerned with the patients' personal and social problems as well as their health problems. Where appropriate, GPs refer patients to hospitals or clinics, or other agencies, for specialist services.

General practice differs from other areas of medicine as GPs are not salaried. GPs receive a basic allowance plus additional payments depending on the number of patients registered with them and the types of service they offer.

Most GPs work as part of a team, the size of the team depending on the number of doctors working together and the variety of other professionals working with them (e.g. practice nurses, counsellors, receptionists, etc). However, much of their time is spent on a one-to-one basis with the patients. GPs often work long hours, seeing patients at their surgery or visiting them at home when necessary.

Talk it over

Do GPs and nurses need similar qualities for their work with people?

Jobs in the direct provision of social care

People who work in social care may be employed by public, private or voluntary organisations. They may undertake residential work, day care or 'fieldwork'. **Fieldwork** is the term used when a worker operates from a base (usually an office) but goes out to meet people, sometimes in their own homes ('working in the field'). As with health care, many other people are employed in jobs that support the direct provision of care (such as clerks and catering staff) but who may not come into direct contact with the clients.

Care assistants

Care assistants often provide **social care**. Most care assistants are employed by Local Authorities but they are increasingly being employed in the private sector as Local Authorities move away from the direct provision of services to the purchasing of private care services. Care assistants often work in residential homes, day centres, day nurseries or in people's own homes. Hence they work with people in a variety of ways and in various settings. Numerous other people are also employed in jobs that are concerned with people's social welfare (see Figure 1.25).

Care assistants assist people who require help with everyday tasks, such as getting up, washing, bathing, going to the toilet, dressing, shopping and housework. Obviously these tasks vary according to the individual client: care assistants can work with children and young people, people with

A care assistant who works with the elderly

CASE STUDY – Catherine

Catherine is a nurse on a hospital ward for elderly people. This is how she describes a typical day's work:

'I started work this morning at 7.00 am. When I came on to the ward many of the patients were already awake. This ward is for women only but in other hospitals the wards sometimes have both men and women. There are twenty beds on this ward grouped in bays of four. In some older hospitals the beds are just in lines down two sides of a long, narrow ward. The patients on this ward have a variety of problems: some are recovering from heart attacks or strokes, others have progressive illnesses such as motor neurone disease or Parkinson's disease, others have cancer.

My day begins with a "hand-over" from the night staff, who tell us how each patient has been during the night. It is then very hectic as the breakfast trolley arrives, and then we have to go round with the patients' medication. After this, the patients want to have a wash or bath. Later, various members of the multi-disciplinary team start arriving, such as the doctor, physiotherapist, social worker and occupational therapist. If we are beginning to plan a patient's discharge, there is often a meeting of the multi-disciplinary team to discuss how plans are going; often this also includes the patient and her relatives.

During the morning a patient may need to go to one of the other units for treatment, and I will often accompany her. Several of our patients have to have their blood pressure taken every 4 hours and those who are diabetic will need their blood sugar levels tested; others may need their dressings changed. Sometimes during the morning I will have a break for about 15 minutes but then it's back to the ward to help make beds, help the patients' get to

the toilet, answer patients' and relatives' queries about medication, etc. Patients are sometimes very anxious about what is happening to them and need a lot of reassurance and explanation from us. At the end of the shift, after the patients have all had their lunch and we've been round with the medication again, it's time to record what has been happening on each patient's file and to hand over to the afternoon shift. I love the work very much but it can be very tiring.'

Questions

1   What tasks might Catherine perform as part of her duties as a nurse?

2   What is meant by a multi-disciplinary team?

3   What skills does a ward nurse need in order to carry out his or her role?

'I love the work very much ...'

Figure 1.25   A few of the main jobs in social care

Social workers	Care workers	Counsellers	Others
Children and families	Residential care	People with AIDS	Community workers
Older people	Day care	Bereavement	Housing officers
People with disabilities	Home care	Drugs and alcohol	Instructors
People with learning disabilities	People with disabilities	Family work	Liaison officers
People with mental health problems	People with learning disabilities	General counselling	Probation officers
Medical social workers	People with AIDS	Marital problems	Social work assistants
Palliative care social workers	Children and families	Students	Wardens
People with AIDS		Teenagers	

CASE STUDY – Pamela

Pamela is a care assistant in a residential home for older people. This is how she describes a typical day's work:

'Today I started work at 7.00 am. This means I was there when the residents began to wake up. The home I work in has forty residents and there are four units, so that 10 people live in each unit. There are six single bedrooms in each unit and two double rooms. One of the units, Snowdrop unit, is mainly for people with dementia.

Today I worked in Primrose unit where there are five women, three men and a married couple. My first task of the day was to help get people up, and to help them toilet, wash and dress. There are three assistants on the unit first thing in the morning, as this is a busy time. Once people are ready I help with the breakfasts. One of the three ladies I mainly work with is unable to feed herself, so I help her with this. Once breakfast is over the residents like to do various things. Some listen to the radio or watch TV, but when the weather is fine, like it was today, some like to go out into the garden. I took Joe out in his wheelchair this morning for a stroll around the grounds.

Throughout the morning people will need help with various things, such as going to the toilet or having a bath. Much of my time is taken up with toileting, washing and with meal times, but it's really nice when there is time to talk with a resident. They often have very interesting stories to tell.'

Questions

1   How might a care assistant help the residents who live in the home?

2   How could you find out about services for older people in your area?

'The residents often have very interesting stories to tell'

physical or learning disabilities and with older people.

Some of the tasks include helping people with their personal hygiene (washing, bathing, cleaning their teeth, washing their hair, etc.). The tasks may also involve domestic duties (such as washing up, making beds, ironing, preparing and cooking meals, shopping, etc.). Sometimes care assistants will help people to learn new skills, including budgeting and cooking. They may also help set up activities for their clients that will help them improve or maintain their independence; they will also provide friendly support and a listening ear.

As already mentioned, care assistants can work in a variety of settings (nursing and residential homes, day centres, hostels and group homes or in the client's own home as a home carer). Hence a care assistant's working hours can vary greatly. Those working in a day centre will often work regular hours, Monday to Friday. However those working in a residential home, hostel or group home may be required to work shifts, sometimes starting early in the morning and finishing early in the afternoon, or starting in the afternoon and working through the evening. They may also have to work over weekends and at bank holidays. Care assistants working in the clients' own homes may work split shifts (i.e. a few hours in the morning and again in the evening). Many care assistants work part time.

Skills and qualities

Care assistants must be able to work with people from all sorts of backgrounds, religions, cultures and of different ages. They will need to be able to work alone and as part of a team. Maturity and common sense are very important. They must also have the right attitude and personality to be able to work with frail people, people with disabilities or with people who have difficulty doing everyday tasks. Patience, tolerance and the ability to encourage clients to do for themselves those things they are able to do are similarly very important.

Social workers

The majority of social workers are employed by Local Authorities although some may be employed by the health service or by voluntary organisations,

Social workers might work with people who have physical disabilities

such as the National Society for the Prevention of Cruelty to Children (NSPCC). The role of the social worker is to help people of all ages who need support with various aspects of their lives. These problems may be connected to low incomes, unemployment , poor housing, difficulties due to illness, disability, old age or relationship problems. As already noted, most social workers are employed by Local Authority social services departments (England and Wales), social work departments (Scotland) and area health and social services boards (Northern Ireland). They often work in teams that specialise in working with particular client groups, such as children and families, older people, people with physical disabilities, people with learning disabilities or people with mental health problems.

Social workers aim to assess the needs of individuals and families, then to set up and co-ordinate the services required to meet those needs. For example, a young adult who has had a road traffic accident, which results in him or her having to use a wheelchair, may need someone to help with personal care (getting up, washed, and dressed), someone to help with household tasks (cleaning, shopping, laundry) and may need special transport to get about. Sometimes the team includes other professionals, such as occupational therapists, home carers and clerks.

Social workers working with children and families might specialise in fostering and adoption work, in cases where child abuse or neglect is suspected or in cases where children have special needs (for example, when the child has a disability or behavioural problems). Social workers involved in child care may be required to attend juvenile courts.

When appropriate, social workers meet their clients and families to assess their needs and to determine the short and longer-term courses of action. Sometimes this can be done quickly and easily, but in other instances careful assessment and planning over a long period of time may be required. Social workers need to build up a relationship of trust with their clients so that they can help their clients explore the options open to them and to make informed choices about how their needs can best be met.

Social workers often work on a one to one basis with their clients, but at other times they will work with whole families or groups of people who have specific needs. They may also help clients to help themselves – in setting up support groups or self-help groups.

Some social workers specialise in other areas of work, for example:

◦ medical social work

◦ social work in palliative care

◦ work with people who have HIV and AIDS

◦ helping people who are drug or alcohol dependent

◦ work with people who have eating disorders

◦ helping women who have been abused.

These social workers often provide ongoing emotional support to the people they work with. Many social workers who choose to specialise work for voluntary organisations, but some might work for the NHS.

Most social workers work a 36-hour week, Monday to Friday. However, they are required to be flexible in their working hours, which can sometimes involve evening and, occasionally, weekend working.

Skills and qualities

Social workers deal with all sorts of people, from different backgrounds, religions, cultures and of different ages. They therefore need to respect

Talk it over

Do you know someone who has been assessed, or has received help from a social worker?
What sort of help did he or she need and how was this need met?

individuals' personal beliefs, identities and the choices they make. They also need to be very good communicators, both verbally and in writing. Although a great deal of time is spent in client contact, there is also a lot of paperwork and administration that must be attended to. Keeping records and writing reports is an important aspect of the social worker's role. To assess people's needs they must be able to:

◦ build up a rapport with people

◦ collect and analyse large amounts of complex information

◦ explain the options available to meet people's needs

◦ negotiate with others in order to obtain the services necessary to meet those needs.

There are often many conflicting demands on the social workers' time. Therefore they must be able to prioritise the tasks they need to do and to be capable of working under pressure. Much of the work can be emotionally demanding, but they must come to understand their clients' problems without getting involved at a personal level. Social workers must be strong enough to deal with a lack of co-operation from some of their clients while still trying to help them (see Figure 1.26).

Think it over

Do you know of anyone who has a learning disability?
What activities is he or she involved in during the week?
Does he or she go to work or attend a course at his or her local college?

Talk it over

What qualities and skills would a care assistant and a social worker have in common?
Make a list of them.

CASE STUDY – Justin

Justin is a social worker in a team which works with people who have learning disabilities. This is how he describes a typical day's work:

'I work in a team where there are four social workers, a social work assistant and three community nurses. Our team leader is also a social worker. This morning began with us all meeting together to talk about any problems we have had in helping the various people we work with and to agree who is to work with the new person who has just been referred to us. This is a 30-year-old woman with mild learning disabilities who has always lived with her parents. A few years ago her father died and now her mother is seriously ill. I have been asked to meet Pat and her mother to talk about how Pat will manage in the future and what sort of support she will need; whether she will be able to remain in the family home or whether she might need to move into a home with other people with learning disabilities.

I met them this afternoon. The meeting was a very emotional one, with Pat's mother having to face up to the fact that she will not be able to look after Pat any longer and Pat having to think about her mother's impending death. Having talked about some of the options, I agree to meet Pat and her mother again in a few days, when they will have had time to think things through.

During the morning I attended a review meeting at a day centre. This centre is for people with learning disabilities and clients got there once a week to meet one another and to have group discussions about any issues that are worrying them. Today we are reviewing the care plan and activity plan of a young man who I've been involved with for the past three years. At the moment he

'The work can be emotionally draining, but it is also very rewarding'

is very unhappy about the computer course he has been attending at the local college and wants to talk about finding an alternative course. Also at the meeting are Ben's parents and his key worker from the day centre. After a lot of discussion Ben decides he would rather be doing an art course. I agree to find out more about these for him.

Sometimes the work can be very frustrating – there aren't enough funds to put in all the support services someone really needs. It can be emotionally draining, but it is also very rewarding!'

Questions

1 What social services might a person with learning difficulties need?

2 What social care services are available in your area for people with learning difficulties?

3 What skills would a social worker need when working with someone who has learning difficulties?

Figure 1.26   The skills and qualities required of a social worker

Jobs in the direct provision of early years services

Local Authorities, voluntary organisations and private agencies are involved in the provision of day care services and playgroups for children aged 5 years and under, and they may also provide out-of-school 'clubs' for children between the ages of 5 and 8 years. The main jobs in early years services include nursery nurses, childminders, and play and playgroup leaders. However, they also include 'nannies' and au pairs who are employed directly by parents, often through agencies. They similarly include other child care professionals, such as educational psychologists.

Other professionals involved in providing appropriate health care services for babies and young children include paediatricians, midwives, health visitors, nurses who specialise in working with ill children, speech therapists, physiotherapists and play therapists.

As in health and social care, there are also many people in jobs that provide support to those giving direct care but who may not come into direct contact with the clients. These include managers of services, secretaries, cooks and cleaners (see Figure 1.27).

Nursery nurses

Nursery nurses can work in a variety of settings, such as day nurseries, residential nurseries,

A nursery nurse

Figure 1.27 A few of the main jobs in early years services

Health care	Social care and early years education	Support staff
Midwives	Play leaders	Managers
Health visitors	Play therapists	Administrators
Paediatric nurses	Social workers	Secretaries
Nannies	Nannies	Cooks
Nursery nurses	Nursery nurses	Cleaners
Speech therapists	Au pairs	
Physiotherapists	Psychologists	
	Childminders	
	Specialist teacher assistants	

schools, crèches, hospitals or in the child's own home. They may work as part of a team (e.g. when working in a nursery) or they may work alone with one or two children or a group of children (i.e. when working privately for a family or when working in a crèche).

Nursery nurses can be involved in many care tasks – for instance, feeding, washing and toileting. They are also responsible for planning activities and play following the guidelines set out in the Early Learning Goals. The Early Learning Goals provide guidance on what children should be able to do at the ages of 3, 4 and 5 years. At the end of the reception year at school (when aged 5–6 years), that is, from school year 1 onwards, the children's learning is planned according to the requirements of the National Curriculum.

Nursery nurses take responsibility for the overall care of the children in their charge.

Skills and qualities
The children may come from all sorts of backgrounds and from different ethnic or religious groups. Nursery nurses therefore need to respect the different beliefs and values of the children's families. They also need good communication skills, especially with the children but also with the adults: they will often need to talk with the parents about their children. They similarly need good writing skills as they will be required to write reports on the children's development and achievements. Patience is a very necessary quality as children can be very demanding, and some may have emotional or

behavioural problems. Nursery nurses must have an understanding of child development and of the principles of preschool education. Sometimes they work alongside other professionals, such as social workers, speech therapists or physiotherapists, and so need to be able to work as part of a multi-disciplinary team. Nursery nurses also need a lot of energy, as children can be very active (see Figure 1.28).

Figure 1.28 The skills and qualities required of a nursery nurse

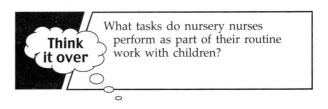

Think it over

What tasks do nursery nurses perform as part of their routine work with children?

Talk it over

Nursery nurses and social workers need similar skills and qualities. What are they? Make a list of them.

What are the different skills and qualities each need?

Jobs providing indirect care

To care for their clients effectively, those people who provide direct care often need the help of support services. In hospitals, clinics, social services departments and early years services, all sorts of administrative staff are needed. In

CASE STUDY – Lynn

Lynn is a nursery nurse in a private day care nursery. This is how she describes a typical day's work:

'The nursery opens at eight o'clock in the morning and closes at six o'clock at night. It is open from Monday to Friday every week of the year and only closes for bank holidays. All the children live in the local community and come from various ethnic backgrounds. Many come to the nursery because their parents are at work. About half come from one-parent families. The children are aged from 18 months to 5 years.

My day begins by greeting the children. Today, a new 3-year-old little boy came for the first time. He was very upset when his mother left and I stayed with him until he stopped crying and joined in with the other children. We give the children breakfast at about 9.00 am, dinner at 12.30 and afternoon tea at 4.00 pm. I sometimes help serve the food and I help the younger children to feed themselves. I am involved in all aspects of the children's routine care, including washing, dressing and toileting.

After breakfast I help set out the play equipment, such as colouring or picture books, jigsaws and puzzles, dressing-up clothes and toys. If the weather is good we go out into the garden where there are swings, slides, climbing frames and sand trays. After lunch we have 'quiet time'. I often read a story to the children before they have a rest. We have little beds where

'I feel I am a friend to many of the children'

the children can have a nap. Later in the afternoon we often sing songs or play games. I also help the children to learn how to tie their shoe-laces and about table manners and other social skills.

It is a very demanding job. Sometimes the children can be quite naughty and will not listen to what is being said to them. You need a lot of patience. You also need a lot of energy to keep up with them. But it is also a very rewarding job and I feel I am a friend to many of the children.'

Questions

1 What qualifications does a nursery nurse have to have?

2 What skills does a nursery nurse need in order to work with small children?

3 What services are available in your area for pre-school age children?

residential and day care centres, whether run by Health Authorities or Local Authorities, catering services and possibly laundry services are required. As new technology is increasingly being employed in health care services, the equipment used for diagnosis and treatment is becoming ever more sophisticated. Similarly, information technology is now used for recording service users' records, which means that staff must be employed who have specialist technical skills (see Figure 1.29).

Receptionists

Receptionists are to be found working in many health and social care units, and their roles will vary according to the setting where they are employed. However, the receptionist's basic tasks remain the same and they usually involve operating the telephone switchboard and greeting people as they arrive at the unit. Sometimes they are also required to do general clerical tasks or to take on administrative or secretarial duties. They must also be able to use a computer for sending out letters and to keep the unit's information up to date.

Skills and qualities

Receptionists must be able to put people at their ease and to greet them with courtesy and warmth. They should be very sensitive to other people's feelings and be able to cope with people

Receptionists in a GP's surgery

Figure 1.29 A few of the jobs indirectly involved in health, social and early years services

Job
Ambulance drivers
Porters
Catering assistants
Cooks
Domestic staff
Gardeners
Caretakers
Laboratory technicians
Radiographers
Drivers
Managers
Administrators
Secretaries
Clerks
Receptionists
Record keepers
IT officers
Finance officers
Supplies officers
Personnel officers

who are upset. They must be very clear in their communication, both verbally and written. Patience is also very important when dealing with people, and it often helps to have a good sense of humour. As already mentioned, the particular skills a receptionist will need will depend on the requirements of his or her job (see Figure 1.30)

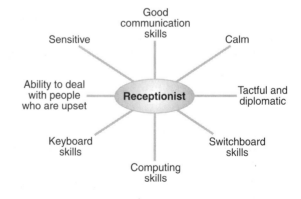

Figure 1.30 The skills and qualities required of a receptionist

Think it over

Make a list of the different offices or establishments you visit that employ a receptionist.

Try it out

Choose one of the job roles you have just read about or you know about and write a short description of the skills needed. Which skills do you think are the most important, and why? You could interview someone working in this sector and base your description on his or her job.

CASE STUDY – John

John is a receptionist in a hospice. This is how he describes his work:

'There are three receptionists at the hospice where I work, and I am the only man among them! One works on Saturdays and Sundays from 9.00 am to 5.00 pm. I work Monday to Friday from 8.00 am to 4.00 pm and the third works Monday to Friday from 4.00 pm until 9.00 pm.

A lot of my time is spent answering the telephone. Sometimes it is a relative who needs to speak to the nurses or a doctor. Sometimes it's another professional who needs to speak to one of the hospice staff. We have lots of different professionals working at the hospice. These include doctors, nurses, social workers, occupational therapists, physiotherapists and a chaplain. I often have to take messages when staff are not available.

The other main part of my job is greeting people when they come to the hospice. Often relatives who are visiting patients can be very upset, and I sometimes have to spend some time talking to them. I often make them a cup of tea.

Part of my role involves selling cards and small gift items to people. This is one way we help to raise money for the hospice. People often bring in donations as well. It is part of my job to receive these donations.

'I am often the first person in the hospice people have contact with'

Even small amounts of money help, so I like to make everyone who brings in a donation feel really special. I am also responsible for sending out "thank you" letters to these people.

I feel the work I do is very important, as I am often the first person in the hospice people have contact with.'

Questions

1 What skills are needed by someone working as a receptionist?

2 What tasks might a receptionist perform?

Effective communication skills

The main skill a care worker needs to work effectively is the availability to understand and communicate with others. Communication skills are vital in care work because they enable care workers to:

⋄ understand the needs of others

⋄ form relationships with clients

⋄ show respect towards clients and other members of staff

⋄ meet the clients' social, emotional and intellectual needs.

Some people might think that 'communicating with clients' involves nothing more than common sense. This is not true: care workers have to develop a range of skills (Figure 1.31).

Being an effective carer involves learning about the individual people you work with. Learning about other people involves listening to what they have to say and understanding the messages people send with their body language. It is not always easy to get to know people: we need the skills of being able to listen, of being capable of sustaining a conversation and of interpreting other people's body language correctly to help us understand each other and to build relationships.

Non-verbal communication

Immediately we meet someone we are usually able to tell what that person is feeling – whether that person is tired, happy, angry, sad, frightened – even before he or she has said anything. We can usually tell what people are feeling by noting their body language.

The proper term for body language is 'non-verbal communication'. Non-verbal means without words, so non-verbal communication is the messages we send out without putting them into words. We send out messages using our eyes, the tone of our voice, our facial expression, our hands and arms, by gestures with our hands and arms, through the angle of our head and by the way we sit or stand (the latter is known as body posture).

When people are sad they may signal this emotion with eyes that look down – there may

Figure 1.31 The communication skills needed for care work

also be tension in their faces, their mouths may be closed. The shoulder muscles are likely to be relaxed but the person's face and neck may show tension. A happy person will have 'wide eyes' that make contact with you – his or her face will 'smile'. When people are excited they move their arms and hands to signal their excitement (Figure 1.32).

Figure 1.32 We signal our emotions through the expression on our faces

Most people are able to recognise such emotions but skilled carers must go one stage further than simply identifying emotions: they must understand the messages they send out with their *own* bodies when working with other people.

> **Think it over**
> When you were young you may have made faces in a mirror – just to see what kinds of expression you could invent. Increasing our sensitivity to our own non-verbal messages can be achieved in a similar way but instead of looking in a mirror we must look closely at how other people react to us – other people become our mirror. If we are trying to look interested in what a client is saying to us, does the client react as if we are interested? If we feel happy, do other people react as if we are happy?

Non-verbal messages

Our bodies send out messages to other people – often without us consciously meaning to send these messages. Some of the most important body areas that send out messages are shown in Figure 1.33.

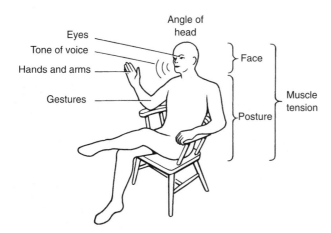

Figure 1.33   Areas of the human body that send out non-verbal messages

The eyes

We can often tell what other people's feelings and thoughts are by looking at their eyes. Our eyes get wider when we are excited, or when we are attracted or interested in someone else. A fixed stare may send the message that someone is angry. In European culture, to look away is often interpreted as being bored or not interested.

The face

Our face can send very complex messages and we can read these easily – even in diagrammatic form (see Figure 1.34).

Figure 1.34   Facial expressions that send out messages

Tone of voice

It's not just *what* we say, but it's the *way* we say it. If we talk in a loud voice with a fixed voice tone, people think we are angry. A calm, slow voice with a varying tone may give out the message that we are being friendly.

Body movement

The way we walk, move our heads, sit, cross our legs and so on sends messages about whether we are tired, happy, sad or bored.

Posture

The way we sit or stand can send messages (Figure 1.35). Sitting with crossed arms can mean 'I'm not taking any notice'. Leaning can send the message you are relaxed or bored. Leaning forward can show you are interested.

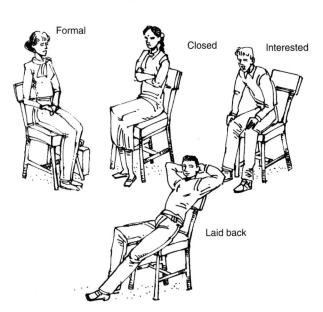

Figure 1.35 **Our body posture can send out messages**

Figure 1.36 **Some gestures commonly used in Britain**

Muscle tension

The tension in our feet, hands and fingers can tell others how relaxed or tense we are. If people are very tense their shoulders might stiffen, their face muscles tighten and they might sit or stand rigidly. A tense face might have a firmly closed mouth, with lips and jaws clenched tight. A tense person might breathe quickly and become flushed.

Gestures

Gestures are hand and arm movements that can help us to understand what a person is trying to say. Some gestures carry a meaning of their own (see Figure 1.36).

Touch

Touching another person can send messages of care, affection, power over that person or sexual interest. The social setting and other body language usually help people to understand what a particular touch might mean. Carers should not make assumptions about touch: even holding someone's hand might be interpreted as an attempt to dominate them!

How close people are

The space between people can show us how friendly or 'intimate' the conversation is.

Different cultures have different codes of behaviour with respect to the space between people when they are talking.

Face-to-face positions

Standing or sitting eye to eye to someone else can send the message of formality or anger. A slight angle will create a more relaxed and friendly feeling (see Figure 1.37).

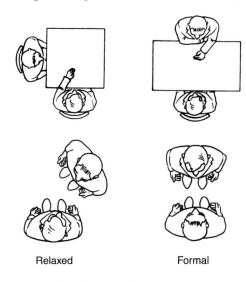

Relaxed   Formal

Figure 1.37 **Face-to-face encounters**

Organising a conversation

Skilled communication involves thinking about how we start and how we finish a conversation. Usually we start with a greeting or by asking how the other person is. As conversations have a beginning, a middle and an end, we must create the right kind of atmosphere for a conversation from the very start. We might need to help someone relax by showing we are friendly and relaxed. Next comes the conversation. When we end the conversation we usually say something like 'See you soon'. When we end a conversation we must leave the other person with the right feelings about what we have said (see Figure 1.38). A conversation is rather like a sandwich: the beginning and ends are the 'bread' and the conversation itself – the middle – is the 'filling'.

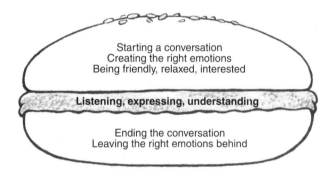

Figure 1.38   The conversation 'sandwich'

The communication cycle

Communication is not just about giving people information. While we talk we go through a process or 'cycle' of:

* hearing what the other person says
* watching the other person's non-verbal messages
* having emotional feelings
* beginning to understand the other person
* sending a message back to the other person.

The communication cycle or process might look something like Figure 1.39.

Listening skills

We might be able to understand other people's emotions by observing their non-verbal

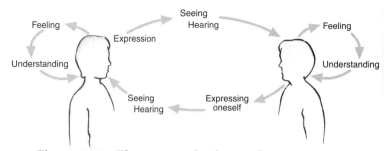

Figure 1.39   The communication cycle

communication but we can't usually understand what's on someone's mind without being a good listener.

Listening is not the same as hearing the sounds people make when they talk. Listening skills involve hearing another person's words – then thinking about what they mean – then thinking what to say back to the other person. Some people call this process 'active listening'. As well as thinking carefully and remembering what someone says, good listeners will also make sure their non-verbal communication demonstrates interest in the other person.

Skilled listening involves:

1   looking interested and ready to listen
2   hearing what is said
3   remembering what is said
4   checking understanding with the other person.

Try it out

This is a practical exercise in listening: Take a piece of paper. Divide it into four areas and write four headings: 'Where I live', 'My last birthday', 'Something to look forward to' and 'My favourite lesson'. Any four titles will do as long as you have lots to say about the four areas. Think about what you can tell another person about yourself based on these four areas. Then get together with a partner who has also planned a talk about him or herself in this way. Describe the four areas to each other. See what you can remember about the other person from what he or she said and how detailed and how accurate this is!

How good are you at understanding and remembering?

Checking our understanding

It is usually easier to understand people who are similar to ourselves. We can learn about different people by checking our understanding of what we have heard.

Checking our understanding involves hearing what the other person says and asking the other person questions. Another way to check our understanding is to put what a person has just said into our own words and to say this back to them to see if we did understand what they said.

When we listen to complicated details of other people's lives, we often begin to form mental pictures based on what they are telling us. Listening skills involve checking these mental pictures to make sure we are understanding correctly. It can be very difficult to remember accurately what people tell us if we don't check how our ideas are developing.

Good listening involves thinking about what we hear while we are listening and checking our understanding as the conversation goes along. Sometimes this idea of checking our understanding is called 'reflection', because we reflect the other person's ideas (Figure 1.40).

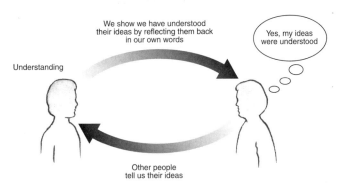

Figure 1.40   'Reflecting' back to the other person proves we have listened

Good listening is hard work. Instead of just being around when people speak, we must build up an understanding of the people around us. Although listening is difficult, people who are attracted to work in care usually enjoy learning about other people and their lives.

Cultural differences

Listening is one of the main ways we usually learn about other people, but skilled carers use a range of conversational techniques when working with clients. These techniques include being sensitive to cultural differences and social contexts, and getting a conversation going and keeping it going.

Culture means the history, customs and the ways people learn as they grow up. The expressions people use and the meanings non-verbal signs can have vary from one culture to another. For example, people from different regions of Britain use different expressions. In parts of the North of England, for example, the word 'canny' means a 'with it' and/or attractive person. In the South this word is unlikely to be understood and may be taken to mean something bad. In Ireland the term 'good crack' means 'good fun', but in England the term 'crack' refers to a very dangerous drug!

White middle-class people often expect other people to 'look them in the eye' while talking. If someone looks down or away a great deal, this is interpreted as a sign that they may be dishonest, or perhaps sad or depressed. In other cultures, for example, among some black communities, looking down or away when talking is a sign of respect – a way of showing you are using your listening skills! Care workers must be careful not to assume that statements and signs always mean the same thing – culture, race, class and geographical location can alter meaning.

There is a vast range of meanings that can be inferred from different types of eye contact, facial expression, posture or gesture and every culture develops its own special system of meanings. It may be impossible to learn about all these possible meanings but carers must be alert to them and must respect them.

Having said all this, it is possible to learn what your clients mean when they communicate with you. One way to do this is to remember what people say or do and try to understand what they really mean. However, this understanding needs to be checked. To do this it is usually possible to ask polite questions, or to work out what people mean over time by watching and listening to the other things they say or do.

The important thing to remember is that our own way of behaving and communicating is not the only way – or even the right way!

Keeping a conversation going

Once we have started a conversation we must keep it going long enough to meet our purpose and the emotional needs of others. Skills that help us achieve this are turn-taking, using non-verbal communication to show interest, the skilful use of questions and using silence at the appropriate moments.

If we are trying to get to know someone, we will probably listen more than we will talk: we must give the person we are talking to the opportunity to express him or herself. This involves taking turns. The person we are talking to will give us clues about this: people often slow down the rate at which they speak when they are reaching their last words, and they might change the tone of voice slightly, and look away from us. They might then stop speaking and look directly at us. If we are sensitive to these messages, we will be ready to ask a question or say something which keeps the conversation going.

We must also be interested in what the other person is saying. This demonstrates to the person we are talking to that we respect them – and carers must be interested in and respect what their clients say.

Showing interest means giving the other person your full attention and is the way you will keep the other person talking. Non-verbal messages we can employ to do this include:

- eye contact – looking at the other person's eyes

- smiling – looking friendly rather than 'cold' or 'frozen' in expression

- hand movements and gestures that show that we are interested

- slight head nods while talking to signal non-verbally, that we 'see', 'understand' or 'agree'.

Asking questions

Some of the questions we might ask will not encourage people to talk: these are closed questions. Questions such as 'How old are you?' are 'closed' because there is only one, right, simple answer the person can give: 'I'm 84'. Closed questions do not lead on to a discussion. 'Do you like butter?' is a closed question because the person replying can only say yes or no. 'Are you feeling well today?' is also closed – the person replying can again only say yes or no.

Open questions 'open' up the conversation. Instead of giving a yes/no answer, the person we are talking to is encouraged to consider his or her reply. A question such as 'How do you feel about the food here?' means the other person has to think about the food and then discuss it. Open questions keep a conversation going; closed questions can block a conversation and cause it to stop.

The more we know about someone, the more sensitive we will be about the questions we ask. For example, people often do not mind answering questions about their feelings or opinions, but dislike questions that ask for personal information. Getting to know people often takes time and will involve a number of short conversations rather than one long, single conversation.

Silence

Pauses in a conversation can be embarrassing – it can look as if we are not listening or interested in what is being said. However, sometimes a silent pause can mean 'let's think' or 'I need time to think'. Silent pauses do not always stop the conversation as long as our non-verbal messages demonstrate to the other people we respect them and are interested in them.

Misusing language

> **Think it over**
>
> Read the short conversation below. Using your knowledge of communication skills, work out what is wrong with them.

A young child is talking with a childminder:

Child: Why do people drive cars?

Childminder: Never mind that, you just keep playing – don't be a nuisance.

A young person with a learning disability is talking with a care worker:

Young person: I can help do it.

Care worker: No you can't help with this, go and help Fran lay the table.

Young person: But I want.

Care worker: No! You do what I tell you.

A care worker is helping an older person to get up in the morning:

Care worker: Come on – time to get up!

Older person: Who are you? Where am I?

Care worker: Come on, I'm in a hurry, your breakfast is waiting.

Older person: Where is my daughter?

Care worker: I don't know – just hurry up.

In these conversations the care workers are not listening. They are hearing what is said but are ignoring the client's feelings. There is no effective communication cycle or conversation. The conversations have no beginning, middle or end. There is no skilled questioning to try to understand what the clients are saying. In each situation people are told to do something with no respect being shown for their needs or feelings.

Barriers to communication

There are three main ways in which communication can become blocked:

1   If a person cannot see, hear or receive the message.

2   If a person cannot make sense of the messages.

> **Think it over**
>
> Children who are not encouraged to ask questions may learn 'not to bother'. This may limit their social and intellectual development. Children whose questions are often ignored may learn to do other things to get attention. Throwing toys, shouting or breaking things may result in getting attention if asking questions does not.

People who are ignored may feel they are of little value. A person who is never listened to may have a poor opinion of him or herself. People with learning difficulties treated this way will have unfulfilled social and emotional needs.

Older people may not be given the respect they deserve. If their questions are ignored they are likely to feel they are not worth much. Without purposeful conversation, they may feel life is not worth living.

Effective care hinges on good communication skills.

3   If a person misunderstands the message.

Apart from visual and hearing disabilities, the first kind of block can be created by environmental problems:

- poor lighting
- noise
- speaking from too far away (Figure 1.41).

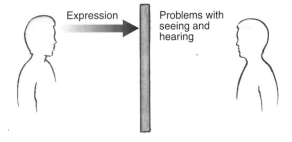

Expression

Problems with seeing and hearing

Figure 1.41   Environmental problems, such as noise and poor lighting, can create communication barriers

Occasions when people might not be able to make sense of messages include the following:

- Different languages are being used, including sign languages.

- People are using different terms, such as **jargon** (technical language), **slang** and **dialect**.

- One of the speakers has a physical or intellectual disability, such as an illness, memory loss, or a learning dysfunction.

Examples of misunderstanding include the following:

- *Cultural differences*: different cultures interpret non-verbal and verbal messages, and humour, in different ways.

- *Assumptions about people*: assumptions about race, gender, disability, etc. can lead to stereotyping and misunderstanding.

- *Emotional differences*: very angry or very happy people may misinterpret what is said.

- *Social contact*: conversations and non-verbal messages understood by close friends may not be understood by strangers.

Supporting individuals

The care **value base** (see the next main section in this unit) requires care workers to value people's equality and diversity as well as their rights. People will feel valued and respected when they have been listened to, and when they feel their needs and wishes have been understood by the care worker. Good communication skills are vital for this, and care workers must find ways of overcoming the communication barriers that often arise between the client and worker (Figure 1.42).

Figure 1.42 Care values are often expressed in our conversations with clients

Ways of overcoming barriers to communication

Visual disability

- Use conversation to describe things.

- Help people to touch things (e.g. touch your face so that the person can recognise you).

- Explain the details sighted people take for granted.

- Check what people *can* see (many registered blind people can see shapes or tell the difference between light and dark).

- Check that spectacles are being worn, if necessary, and that they are clean.

Hearing disability

- Do not shout: speak normally and make sure your face is visible so that those who can lip-read are able to do so.

- Use pictures or write messages.

- Learn to sign – for people who can use signed languages, such as Makaton or British Sign Language (BSL).

- Use the services of a professional communicator or interpreter when sign languages are employed.

- Check that hearing aids etc., are being used and are in working order.

Environmental barriers

- Check and, if necessary, improve the lighting.

- If possible, reduce the background noise.

  Move to a quieter or better-lit room, if this will help.

- Work in smaller groups if this will help you see and hear each other more easily.

Language differences

- Use pictures, diagrams, and non-verbal signs and expressions.

◊ Use a translator or interpreter.

◊ Do not make assumptions or stereotype. Do not assume that people with physical or sensory disabilities have learning disabilities. Similarly, older people who have communication difficulties should not be labelled as 'confused'.

Jargon, slang and dialects

◊ Try different ways of saying things – try to make sense of sounds or words people do not seem to understand.

◊ Speak in short, clear sentences.

Physical and intellectual disabilities (such as learning or memory disability)

◊ Use pictures and signs as well as clear, simple speech.

Be calm and patient.

◊ Set up group meetings where people can share their interests or where they can reminisce.

◊ Make sure that people do not become isolated

Misunderstandings

◊ Be alert to different cultural interpretations.

◊ Avoid making assumptions or discriminating against people who are different.

◊ Use your listening skills to check your understanding is correct.

◊ Stay calm and try to calm people who are angry or excited.

◊ Be clear about the context of your conversation. Is it formal or informal? Use the appropriate form of communication accordingly.

What if it is not possible to communicate with a client?

Sometimes, when people have a very serious learning disability or an illness (such as

dementia), it is not possible to communicate with them. In such situations care services will often employ an **advocate**. An advocate is someone who speaks for someone else: a lawyer speaking for a client in a courtroom is working as an advocate for that person and will argue the client's case. In care work, a volunteer might try to get to know someone who has dementia or a learning disability. The volunteer tries to communicate the client's needs and wants – as the volunteer understands them. Advocates should be independent of the staff team and so can argue for the client's rights without being constrained by what the staff think is easiest or cheapest to do.

> **Think it over**
>
> Think about a care setting, hospital home or day centre you have visited. What barriers to communication have you noticed? Apart from people's disabilities and differences, what communication barriers were created by the environment or by the staff's communication skills and assumptions?

The care value base

All care work is about improving the client's quality of life – and improving the quality of life means meeting people's intellectual, emotional and social needs, as well as their physical needs.

If care is about making life better for clients, then clients should be:

◊ helped to take control or stay in control of their lives

◊ treated as valuable people

◊ given respect and dignity

◊ listened to.

Care values attempt to define the key principles that should guide how carers behave. These principles include the need to respect people and to listen to what people say – even though at times the language used in the principles may seem complex and daunting.

For example, the Care Sector Consortium was a group of people who devised the National Vocational Qualification (NVQ) training

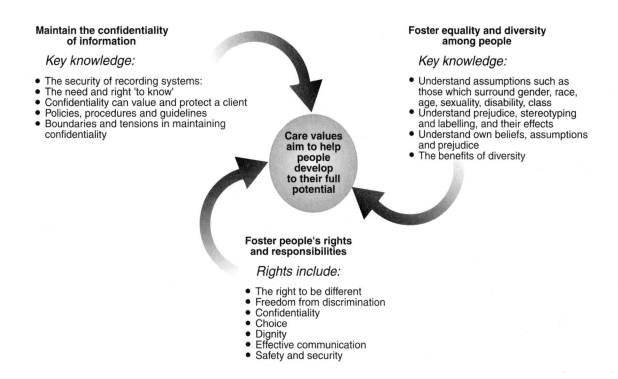

Maintain the confidentiality of information

Key knowledge:

- The security of recording systems:
- The need and right 'to know'
- Confidentiality can value and protect a client
- Policies, procedures and guidelines
- Boundaries and tensions in maintaining confidentiality

Care values aim to help people develop to their full potential

Foster equality and diversity among people

Key knowledge:

- Understand assumptions such as those which surround gender, race, age, sexuality, disability, class
- Understand prejudice, stereotyping and labelling, and their effects
- Understand own beliefs, assumptions and prejudice
- The benefits of diversity

Foster people's rights and responsibilities

Rights include:

- The right to be different
- Freedom from discrimination
- Confidentiality
- Choice
- Dignity
- Effective communication
- Safety and security

Figure 1.43   The care value base

standards for people who work in care. These standards define the values all care workers should follow. These standards are known as the care value base and this is set out in Figure 1.43.

Foster equality and diversity

Carers must value the ways people are different. They must understand the prejudices, stereotypes and assumptions that discriminate people on the grounds of gender, race, age, sexual orientation, disability or class. Carers must prevent such prejudices and assumptions damaging the quality of care provided to clients.

Foster people's rights and responsibilities

People have the right to their own beliefs and lifestyles, but no one has the right to damage the quality of other people's lives. This means that rights often come with responsibilities towards other people.

The easiest way to understand this is to think about the issue of smoking. Adults have a right to choose to smoke even though smoking usually damages health and often shortens a person's life. Smokers have a responsibility to make sure their smoke is not breathed in by other people. (See Figure 1.44.) This means that, in most places today, smoking is only allowed in specially designated areas.

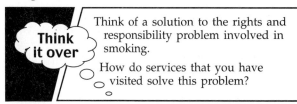

Think it over

Think of a solution to the rights and responsibility problem involved in smoking.

How do services that you have visited solve this problem?

Maintain the confidentiality of information

Confidentiality is an important right for all clients. It is important because of the following reasons:

- Clients may not trust carers if the carers do not keep information confidential.

Figure 1.44 We all have rights, but we also have responsibilities to others

- Clients may not feel valued or may have feelings of low self-esteem if their private details are shared with others

- The client's safety may be put at risk if details of their property or their habits are widely known.

- A professional service that maintains respect for individuals must keep private information confidential.

- There are legal requirements to maintain the confidentiality of personal records.

Trust

Trust is very important. If you know your carer won't pass on things you have said to him or her, you will be more inclined to tell him or her what you really think and feel.

Self-esteem

If your carer promises to keep things confidential, this shows he or she respects and values you; it shows that you matter. Your self-esteem will therefore be higher than if the carer did not keep things confidential.

Safety

You may have to leave your home empty at times. If other people know where you keep your money and when you are out, someone may be tempted to break in. Hence carers must keep personal details confidential to protect their clients' property and personal safety.

Medical practitioners and lawyers have always strictly observed confidentiality as part of their professional code of conduct. If clients are to receive a professional service, care workers must follow this example.

Valuing diversity

No two people are the same and, because people are different, it can be easy to think that some people are better then others or that some views are right while others are wrong. Our individual cultures and life experiences may lead us to make assumptions about what is right or normal. When we meet people who are different from ourselves, it is all too easy to see them as 'not right' or 'not normal'. We must remember that different people see the world in different ways, and that our way of thinking may seem unusual to someone else.

Some of the ways in which people are different from one another are listed in Figure 1.45, which also lists the dangers of discrimination that might arise as a result of these differences.

Figure 1.45 The dangers of discrimination

Difference	Possible discrimination
Age	People may think of others as being children, teenagers, young adults, middle aged or old. Hence discrimination can creep into our thinking if we see some age groups as being 'the best' or if we make assumptions about the abilities of different age groups
Gender	In the past, men often had more rights than women and were seen as more important. Assumptions about gender still create discrimination problems
Race	People may understand themselves as being black or white, as European, African or Asian. People also have specific national identities, such as Polish, Nigerian, English or Welsh. Assumptions about racial or national characteristics lead to discrimination
Class	People differ in their upbringing, the kind of work they do and the money they earn. People also differ in the lifestyles they lead and the views and values that go with levels of income and spending habits. Discrimination against others can be based on their class or lifestyle
Religion	People grow up in different religious traditions. For some people, spiritual beliefs are at the centre of their understanding of life. For others, religion influences the cultural traditions they celebrate – for example, many Europeans celebrate Christmas even though they might not see themselves as practising Christians. Discrimination can take place when people assume that their customs or beliefs should apply to everyone else
Sexual orientation	Many people consider their sexual orientation as very important to understanding who they are. Gay and lesbian relationships are often discriminated against. Heterosexual people sometimes judge other relationships as 'wrong' or abnormal
Ability	People may make assumptions about what is 'normal'. Hence people with physical disabilities or learning disabilities may be labelled as 'not normal' or others may have stereotypical views about what they are capable of doing
Health	People who develop illnesses or mental health problems may feel they are valued less by others; they may feel discriminated against
Relationships	People choose many different lifestyles and have different emotional commitments, such as marriage, having children, living in a large family, living a single lifestyle but having sexual partners, or being single and not being sexually active. People live in different family and friendship groups. Discrimination can happen when people think that one lifestyle is 'right' or best
Presentation and dress	People express their individuality, lifestyle and social role through their clothes, hairstyles, make-up and jewellery. While it may be important to conform to dress codes at work, it is also important not to make stereotypical judgements about people because of the way they dress

Learning about diversity

To learn about other people's cultures and beliefs, we must take great care to listen to and observe what other people say and do. While learning about different cultures and beliefs can be very interesting and exciting, some people can find it stressful: we may feel our own culture and beliefs are being challenged when we realise there are so many different lifestyles. Such feelings may block our ability to learn about others.

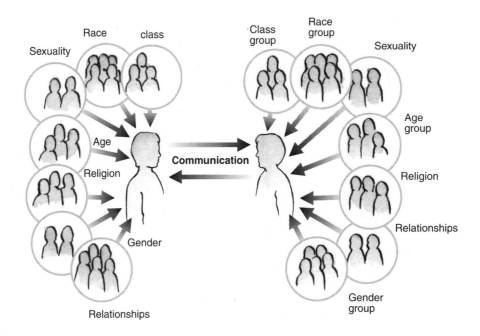

The groups a person belongs to will influence his or her beliefs and behaviour

Skilled carers must get to know the people they work with so that they will not make false assumptions about them. Carers must understand the ways that class, race, age, gender and so on influence individual people. Carers should also remember that a person's behaviour is not 'fixed': it will change as that person moves from one social group to another. For example, when we are at work we tend to take on the values of our workplace – we think and behave in the way our work demands and in the way our colleagues and those we come into contact with expect. In our private lives, however, we will take on other values: those of our friends when out for the evening or those of our family when at home or when we return for a family celebration.

Individuals may belong to the same ethnic group but they might have different religions or belong to different class groups. Simply knowing what someone's religion is will not necessarily tell you all about that person's beliefs or general culture. We can learn about different ethnic and religious customs but is impossible for us to know all the differences that might exist among individual clients. As mentioned earlier, the best way to learn about diversity is to listen to and communicate with people whose lives are different from our own.

Valuing diversity may make your own life better

Valuing diversity will enrich your life. If you are open to other people's life experience and differences, you will become more flexible and creative because you can imagine how other people see things. You will develop a wider range of social skills, and learning about other cultures will provide you with new experiences. Understanding other people's lives may also help you adapt your own lifestyle when you have to cope with change. For example, if you talk to people who are married or who have children, you will be better prepared if you choose these roles for yourself.

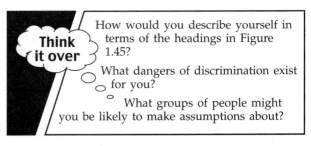

Think it over

How would you describe yourself in terms of the headings in Figure 1.45?

What dangers of discrimination exist for you?

What groups of people might you be likely to make assumptions about?

Employers are also likely to want to employ people who value diversity for the following reasons:

* Effective non-discriminatory care depends on all staff valuing diversity.

* People who value diversity are likely to be flexible and creative.

* People who value diversity will form good relationships with their colleagues and with the clients.

* Diverse teams often work together more effectively. If everyone has the same skills and interests, the team members may compete with each other. If people have different interests it is more likely the team will do all the work required and the people in the team will enjoy working together.

In care settings, everyone should receive a service of equal quality that meets their own personal needs. This is not, however, the same as everyone receiving the same service. Treating people as individuals, taking into account their different beliefs, abilities, likes and dislikes, is at the heart of caring for others.

If you encounter a situation where the services are not of equal quality, you should bring this to the attention of the management. In care settings there should be policies that have been designed to protect people from discrimination (see below).

Rights and responsibilities

Government legislation, codes of practice, employers' policies and national training standards outline the rights clients have when they are receiving health and social care services. These rights include:

* freedom from discrimination

* a right to independence and choice

* the right to be respected and to retain one's dignity

* safety and security

* confidentiality.

Figure 1.46 outlines some examples of these rights and responsibilities in more detail.

Freedom from discrimination

Discrimination means treating some groups of people less well than others and it may appear in the following ways:

* **Physical abuse** (hitting, pushing, kicking or otherwise assaulting a person). People may assault others because they hate certain groups or simply because they feel frustrated or annoyed at those who are different from themselves.

* **Verbal abuse** (insults, 'put downs' or damaging language). As with physical abuse, verbal abuse may make individuals feel more powerful if they think they can hurt other people with words.

* **Neglect** occurs when people are discriminated against by being ignored or by not being offered the help others might receive.

* **Exclusion** is a more subtle form of discrimination and may be hard to prove. Exclusion means stopping people from

Figure 1.46 The rights and responsibilities of people receiving care

Rights	Responsibilities
Not to be discriminated against	Not to discriminate against others
To have control and independence in their own lives	To help others to be independent and not try to control other people
To make choices and take some risks	Not to interfere with others, or put others at risk
To maintain their own beliefs and lifestyles	To respect the different beliefs and lifestyles of others
To be valued and respected	To value and respect others
A safe environment	To keep things safe for others
Confidentiality in personal matters	To respect confidentiality for others

getting services or jobs because they belong to a certain class, race or other group. Disabled people may be excluded from certain services because access is difficult – some buildings still do not have full disabled access. Some jobs may not be advertised in all areas, therefore excluding certain communities.

* **Avoidance** is where people try to avoid sitting next to people or working with people who are different from themselves. Such people are trying to avoid contact – perhaps because they do not want to learn about or rethink any of their prejudices.

* **Devaluing** means seeing some people as less valuable than others. Some people's self esteem is raised because they receive praise and their ideas are valued, but those who are 'different' may be criticised and their ideas ignored. People who are subjected to constant discrimination and prejudice may develop a very low sense of their own self-worth.

The effects of discrimination

Discrimination in all forms has permanent and extremely damaging effects (see Figure 1.47).

Figure 1.47   The effects of discrimination and abuse

Independence and choice

Although we all think of ourselves as being independent, there are times in our lives when we need another person's help. In care settings we can increase clients' independence by giving them control and choice over certain aspects of their care. To do this we must recognise the difference between doing things *to* or *for* clients and doing things *with* clients.

Wherever possible, clients should be helped to take control over their care. Even when people cannot do things for themselves, they can still be asked for their opinions about how they would like to be treated. This way we **empower** clients: feelings of independence increase a client's self-esteem. Feeling dependent on others may cause the opposite: clients will feel vulnerable and will have low self-esteem.

Talk it over

Discuss the difference between working *with* clients and working to do things *for* clients. Make a poster of *do's* and *don'ts* that shows how you could empower clients to be independent.

Dignity

Imagine you have been involved in an accident that puts you in hospital. Before this accident you were in control of yourself – you could do things for yourself – but now you need help with such basic things as washing and going to the toilet. How would you feel if someone had to help you to use the toilet? Perhaps if that person showed respect for your feelings and treated you with dignity, you might not feel so bad.

Clients must be treated with respect: when helping clients eat, wash, dress or use the toilet, it is vital we allow them to retain their sense of self-worth and dignity. We must show respect in the ways we give support. We must not have negative attitudes and we must provide the clients with the privacy and dignity they deserve.

Safety

All clients have the right to feel safe and secure when they are receiving care. They should not have to worry about themselves or their property; they must remain free of concern. The Health and Safety at Work Act 1974 makes it a duty of

Study this diagram. How many hazards can you spot?

(Answers are given in the 'Answers to tests' section at the end of the book.)

employers to ensure 'the health, safety and welfare at work of employees'. Equally, 'Employees have a duty to take reasonable care for the health and safety of themselves and others'.

When working in care it must be part of our daily routine to assess the safety of all situations. When working with clients who have impaired movement or poor sensory perception, it is doubly important to ensure there are no hazards.

Confidentiality

Confidentiality is a basic human right, but is so important that it has become a specific issue in the value base. The Data Protection Acts 1984 and 1998, the Access to Personal Files Act 1987 and the Access to Health Records Act 1990, make it a legal requirement that health and social care agencies keep client details confidential.

You will often be given personal information about the clients you are caring for, and this information must be kept confidential. Confidential personal information passed on to the wrong people might result in the client being discriminated against or put in danger. If care workers were to pass such information on to friends, neighbours or other members of the public, clients might feel they have lost control

'You can't trust them'

'I don't matter'

'I'm not important to them'

'I'm never telling them anything again'

'Nobody cares about me'

'Professional! That's not professional'

'I don't belong here'

Figure 1.48   The confidentiality of the things clients tell you about is of vital importance

over their lives. For example, imagine your next-door neighbour starts to treat you as though you had a terminal illness when you thought that whatever was ailing you had been getting better. Or have you ever felt really good about yourself, but someone tells you that you look ill? How would you feel now about yourself?

And what of client's property and safety, if their personal details are common knowledge? What could be the consequences if someone says, 'Poor Mrs Jenkins at no. 27 is poorly again, but she leaves the key under the flowerpot by the front door so I can go in and make her a cup of tea'?

Sometimes it is important we tell a manager about a client's personal details, and this is known as 'keeping confidentiality within boundaries'. For example, we must inform managers if clients are at risk of damage to their physical or mental health. We must also tell senior staff of any risks a client may pose to other people, including ourselves. When serious risks are involved, confidentiality might be broken.

Think it over

If you go to see your doctor or go into hospital, you will expect to receive good quality care. What is good quality care?

Different people have different ideas about what constitutes quality. Everyone will say he or she wants the right treatment, but some will also want:

⋄ a nicely decorated room
⋄ peace and quiet
⋄ no waiting.

Others will want:

⋄ friendly conversations with those involved in their care
⋄ time to talk about their problems
⋄ respect.

What do you think is most important?

Codes of practice and charters

Codes of practice and charters help to define the quality of care clients can expect if they receive care services and they can be used as a basis for measuring the quality of care provided.

Codes of practice

What constitutes good care is not a matter of individual debate. Codes of practice are needed to define what quality means. These codes can then be used to measure whether or not a particular service is providing good quality. For example, *Home Life: a Code of Practice for Residential Care*, first published in 1984, has a checklist of 218 recommendations for monitoring the quality of social care. Many of these recommendations have now been built into regulations inspectors check before a residential home can be registered or for a home to remain registered.

Figure 1.49 Some codes of practice mainly give advice and guidance; others can be used to measure the quality of care

The first ten recommendations, which concern staff qualities, are listed in Figure 1.50.

Codes of practice often advise workers on how to behave. For example the Equal Opportunities

STAFF

148 Staff qualities should include responsiveness to and respect for the needs of the individuals.

149 Staff skills should match the residents' needs as identified in the objectives of the home.

150 Staff should have the ability to give competent and tactful care, whilst enabling residents to retain dignity and self-determination.

151 In the selection of staff at least two references should be taken up, where possible from previous employers.

152 Applicants' curriculum vitae should be checked and for this purpose employers should give warning that convictions otherwise spent should be disclosed.

153 Proprietors should consider residents' needs in relation to all categories of staff when drawing up staffing proposals.

154 Job descriptions will be required for all posts and staff should be provided with relevant job descriptions on appointment.

155 In small homes where staff carry a range of responsibilities, these must be clearly understood by staff.

156 Any change of role or duty should be made clear to the member of staff in writing.

157 Minimum staff cover should be designed to cope with residents' anticipated problems at any time.

Figure 1.50 *Home Life*: **recommendations about staff quality**

Commission has published a code to help eliminate sexual discrimination, and the Commission for Racial Equality has issued a code that gives guidance on the elimination of racial discrimination. Similarly, the Department of Health has published a guide to the professional behaviour expected of social workers, doctors and the police when working with people who are mentally ill. These codes do not provide checklists to help in the assessment of qualities. Rather they provide guidelines for service managers when they are devising policies and procedures staff must follow.

1 Social workers will contribute to the formulation and implementation of policies for human welfare, and they will not permit their knowledge, skills or experience to be used to further dehumanising or discriminatory policies and will positively promote the use of their knowledge, skills and experience for the benefit of all sections of the community and individuals.

2 They will respect their clients as individuals and seek to ensure that their dignity, individuality, rights and responsibility shall be safeguarded.

3 They will not discriminate against clients, on the grounds of their origin, race, status, sex, sexual orientation, age, disability, beliefs, or contribution to society, they will not tolerate actions of colleagues or others which may be racist, sexist or otherwise discriminatory, nor will they deny those differences which will shape the nature of clients' needs and will ensure any personal help is offered within an acceptable personal and cultural context. They will draw to the attention of the Association any activity which is professionally unacceptable.

4 They will help their clients both individually and collectively to increase the range of choices open to them and their powers to make decisions, securing the participation, wherever possible, of clients in defining and obtaining services appropriate to their needs

5 They will not reject their clients or lose concern for their suffering, even if obliged to protect themselves or others against them or obliged to acknowledge an inability to help them.

6 They will give precedence to their professional responsibility over their own personal interests.

7 They accept that continuing professional education and training are basic to the practice of social work, and they hold themselves responsible for the standard of service they give.

8 They recognise the need to collaborate with others in the interest of their clients.

9 They will make clear in making any public statements or undertaking any public activities, whether they are acting in a personal capacity or on behalf of an organisation.

10 They will acknowledge a responsibility to help clients to obtain all those services and rights to which they are entitled; and will seek to ensure that these services are provided within a framework which will be both ethnically and culturally appropriate for all members of the community; and that an appropriate diversity will be promoted both in their own agency and other organisations in which they have influence.

11 They will recognise that information clearly entrusted for one purpose should not be used for another purpose without sanction. They will respect the privacy of clients and others with whom they come into contact and confidential information gained in their relationships with them. They will divulge such information only with the consent of the client (or informant) except where there is clear evidence of serious danger to the client, worker, other persons or the community or in other circumstances, judged exceptional, on the basis of professional consideration and consultation.

12 They will work for the creation and maintenance in employing agencies of conditions which will support and facilitate social workers' acceptance of the obligations of the Code.

Figure 1.51 **The BASW principles for social work (taken from the BASW *Code of Ethics*, 1996)**

Most professional bodies have a code of conduct or code of practice which explains the values that guide people who work in that profession. The

Try it out

When you visit a care setting, ask if you can have copies of the setting's policy documents on equal opportunities or confidentiality. How might these documents help to protect the rights of vulnerable people?

Think it over

Compare *Home Life*, the BASW code, and the UKCC code. There are similarities among all three 'codes', but there are also differences because social workers have slightly different responsibilities from nurses.

Pick out three points that are similar in all codes of practice. Why do you think they are there?

British Association for Social Work (BASW) has published 12 principles for social work that are contained within its code of ethics (see Figure 1.51). The UK Central Council for Nursing, Midwifery and Health Visiting (UKCC) has similarly published a 16-point code of professional conduct (see Figure 1.52).

As a registered nurse, midwife or health visitor, you are personally accountable for your practice and, in the exercise of your professional accountability, must:

1 Act always in such a manner as to promote and safeguard the interest and well-being of patients and clients.

2 Ensure that no action or omission on your part, or within your sphere of responsibility, is detrimental to the interests, condition or safety of patients and clients.

3 Maintain and improve your professional knowledge and competence.

4 Acknowledge any limitations in your knowledge and competence and decline any duties or responsibilities unless able to perform them in safe and skilled manner.

5 Work in an open and co-operative manner with patients, clients and their families, foster their independence and recognise and respect their involvement in the planning and delivery of care.

6 Work in a collaborative and co-operative manner with health care professionals and others involved in providing care, and recognise and respect their particular contributions within the care team.

7 Recognise and respect the uniqueness and dignity of each patient and client, and respond to their need for care, irrespective of their ethnic origin, religious beliefs, personal attributes, the nature of their health problems or any other factor.

8 Report to an appropriate person or authority, at least the earliest possible time, any conscientious objection which may be relevant to your professional practice.

9 Avoid any abuse of your privileged relationships with patients and clients and of the privileged access allowed to their person, property, residence or workplace.

10 Protect all confidential information concerning patients and clients obtained in the course of professional practice and make disclosures only with consent, where required by the order of a court or where you can justify disclosure in the wider public interest.

11 Report to an appropriate person or authority, having regard to the physical, psychological and social effects on patients and clients, any circumstances in the environment of care which could jeopardise standards of practice.

12 Report to an appropriate person or authority any circumstances in which safe and appropriate care for patients and clients cannot be provided.

13 Report to an appropriate person or authority where it appears that the health or safety of colleagues is at risk, as such circumstances may compromise standards of practice in care.

14 Assist professional colleagues, in the context of your own knowledge, experience and sphere of responsibility, to develop their professional competence and assist others in the care team, including informal carers, to contribute safely and to a degree appropriate to their roles.

15 Refuse any gift, favour or hospitality from patients or clients currently in your care which might be interpreted as seeking to exert influence to obtain preferential consideration and

16 Ensure that your registration status is not used in the promotion of commercial products or services, declare any financial or other interests in relevant organisations providing such goods or services and ensure that your professional judgement is not influenced by any commercial considerations.

Figure 1.52 The UKCC code of professional conduct

Codes of practice: summary

◦ All codes of practice enable both members of the public and professionals to measure whether quality care is being delivered or not.

◦ *Home Life* includes a checklist to help people assess the quality of care. Other codes are perhaps more abstract but they still help people to decide whether a service is good or not.

◦ Some codes provide professionals with advice and guidelines; others define the detailed values relevant to a specific service.

Talk it over

You are on a placement in a residential nursing home and have noticed that one of the care assistants is 'less than polite' to one of the residents, who speaks hesitantly because of a stammer. The care assistant interrupts the client and often makes choices for the client 'because we haven't got all day'. How would you handle this situation?

1 At coffee time, argue with the assistant about the rights and wrongs of the assistant's behaviour. Or

2 Talk with the client about how the client would like the situation to be handled, offering your support if wanted. Or

3 Go straight to the manager and tell him or her about the incident?

Discuss the pros and cons of each of these three approaches. Which is the best course of action? Is there anything else you could do? Is there a better way to deal with the situation?

Charters

Recent governments have produced a series of charters that outline the standards people can expect from a wide range of services. These charters are like codes of practice but they are designed by Government. The Citizen's Charter, in particular, sets out the quality we can expect from public services. The charter contains information about the services and gives advice about how we can seek redress (chase up our rights) if a service does not fulfil all the stipulated standards. An important section of the Citizen's Charter is the **Patient's Charter**. A new NHS Charter is expected which provides a statement of national standards and offers a localised approach to the services patients can expect.

The existing charter (which was produced in January 1995) set out the rights and standards people could expect of the services (for example, waiting times for out-patient appointments and for operations).

Many GPs are now producing practice charters that give information about the standards of service provided by their particular health centres. These cover such information as opening times, test results collection, how to get a repeat prescription, facilities for people with disabilities and out-of-hours treatment.

The Department of Health requires all Local Authority social services departments to publish **Community Care Charters**. These charters explain what users and carers can expect from the community care services provided in that area are they also set out their services' commitments and standards (see Figure 1.53).

Obtain a copy of the charter your health centre has produced and find out the following information:

1 How could you contact the practice manager for information about his or her job?

2 If you rely on sign language, is there anyone at the surgery who can help you?

3 Suppose someone in your house is pregnant. Will she be able to give birth at home?

4 Is a social worker attached to the practice?

Figure 1.53   Community Care Charters

Unit I Assessment

Obtaining a Pass grade

To *pass* this unit you must produce a report based on two different health and/or social care settings. When writing your report you should use the records you have kept about your visits to or placements in two different settings. If you use your notes or logbook recordings, you should be able to do the following:

1   Describe the types of organisation you have worked in or visited and say whether it was in the statutory, voluntary or private sectors.

2   Describe the client group you have worked with or visited. What needs did the clients have, and why was a care service offered?

3   Describe the roles of two workers. What kind of work do they do? You could perhaps look at one worker in each care setting.

4   Explain how the care value base influences the way each of the two care workers does his or her job.

5   Describe any codes of practice or charters used in the organisation where the workers are based.

6   Demonstrate you have used the relevant communication skills (see below).

7   Explain the possible barriers to communication that might arise when dealing with clients (see below).

Ideas to help with these tasks:

1   You could find out which sector the organisation is in and the needs of its clients from either your tutor or from the senior staff you meet on your visits or placement. Write down the answers as soon as you are given them.

2   Talk to two different workers and make notes about the kind of work they do. If you take a copy of the care value base diagram on page 43 with you, you could show this to the workers and ask them how these values influence the way they do their jobs. Remember to make notes of what they tell you. Also remember to check your notes later that day to make sure you can read and understand them.

3   Ask a senior member of staff or your tutor about the codes of practice and charters that might be relevant to that particular service. You may be able to get a copy from the care setting, from a library or from the Internet. If you have your own copy of a charter or code of practice, this will help you to write about it.

4   Make notes of conversations you have had that demonstrate you have used the relevant communication skills. You could tape record a conversation you have had in college, or you could make notes about a conversation you have with someone in the setting as soon as the conversation has ended. Remember to make notes about your non-verbal behaviour as well as about the things you said. Look back at the communication section earlier in this unit and make a list of the non-verbal messages you used.

5   Ask the care workers in one setting about the barriers to communication they have encountered. Use the communication section given earlier in this unit to help you think about other barriers that might arise. Make a list of barriers that would cause you problems if you were to work with clients yourself.

Obtaining a Merit or Distinction grade.

To obtain a *Merit* or *Distinction* grade, you must analyse the way people do their jobs in the different settings so that you can compare the various ways in which the care value base is implemented.

First, to find out about the jobs people do, interview two different people in the two different settings. You will learn more about their jobs if you ask them about the types of client they mostly work with. The ask them: 'Do the clients you work with all have the same expectations of you?' You will probably discover that different clients have quite different expectations of staff members (see Figure 1.54). Part of the carer's role is to find a way of working that best meets his or her client's different needs. You could ask the workers how they organise their time so that they are able to do all the tasks they are required to perform.

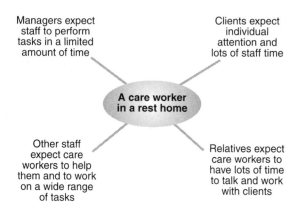

Figure 1.54 The expectations people have of a care worker who works in a rest home

You could then ask the workers to give you examples of how their settings foster diversity, protect the clients' rights and maintain confidentiality. You will probably be given different examples in each setting.

Obtaining a Distinction grade

To obtain a *Distinction*, you must write a detailed account of the care settings and of the work roles undertaken there, and you must explain how the work roles are influenced by the type of organisation the setting is and by the sector it belongs to (statutory, private or voluntary). Classify each of the two care settings you have visited accordingly. Remember to include the setting's size – it might be large (like the NHS or a large national company) or small (such as a voluntary organisation or a private rest home). It is also important to include a description of where the setting is located: in a town or city or in the country.

You will have to ask the staff about the ways the setting's size and nature influences their work with clients. You might also need to speak to a senior manager to learn about the advantages and disadvantages of different sectors and sizes. As well as asking questions, you will be able to learn a great deal just by observing!

Some general questions to consider that might help you prepare your report are as follows:

- How good is the transport to and from the home? Can relatives travel easily?

- How safe is the setting? What security measures are in place? Are crimes such as vandalism and burglary common in the area?

- How easy is it to get to community facilities, (e.g. shops, leisure facilities, temples, mosques, churches, clubs)?

- How easy is it to get staff? Do they have difficult journeys to work? Is it easy to get staff with the right qualifications?

- Look at the sort of resources the organisation can afford to buy. Consider the general condition of the furniture and decorations.

UNIT 1 ASSESSMENT

Skill area	Rating		
	Weakness I am not good at this	**In between** I can improve at this	**Strength** I am good at this
Using listening skills to ckeck I understand other people			
Using open questions			
Understanding the cultural differences in communication			
Being able to keep a conversation going			
Understanding other people's non-verbal messages			
Sending the right non-verbal messages to others			
Organising a conversation with an appropriate beginning, middle and end			

Figure 1.55   My strengths and weaknesses in the communication skills I use

- What sort of staff training and supervision does the organisation provide?

- What sort of equipment is provided for the clients? Are the staff trained to use any new equipment?

- What type of management systems does the organisation have? Do people work in teams? How are duties shared and organised?

Communication
Obtaining a Pass grade

At *Pass* level, you will need to demonstrate relevant communication skills, either in real practical work with clients or in simulation exercises. As well as demonstrating listening, conversation and non-verbal communication skills, you must also explain what the barriers are that can block communication with clients.

Obtaining a Merit grade

To obtain a *Merit* grade, you must explain the communication methods you have chosen to use and must be able to identify your own strengths and weaknesses when communicating.

If you use simulated exercises you could tape record your performance and then analyse the skills you demonstrated. You could use a grid like the one shown in Figure 1.55 to help you assess your strengths and weaknesses. Your grid could be more detailed then the one shown here or it could include other skills than the ones listed in the figure.

When evaluating practical work you should similarly be able to assess your communication skills. For example, you might be able to say: 'Keeping a conversation going is one of my strengths because we talked for

Skill to develop	Action to improve these skill	The way to measure improvements in my skills
1 Listening	(a) Class exercises	Feedback from tutor
	(b) Listening to clients at a day centre	Recording their reaction: do I appear to be a good listener?
2 Understanding cultural differences	Talking to and listening to people from different cultural backgrounds	Listing the different gestures facial expressions and sayings they use
3 Understanding other people's non-verbal messages	Reading a book on body language - looking for real-life examples	Listing examples of non-verbal messages relevant to the clients
4 Sending the right non-verbal messages	Video conversation work with my friends	Listing ideas for changing the expression in my face and eyes so that I look more serious

Figure 1.56   Action plan: improving my communication skills

15 minutes and I kept the conversation going.' Or you might be able to say: 'Understanding other people's non-verbal messages is something I could improve on. I couldn't tell what the person I was talking to felt: her face and body movements didn't send a clear message.' When you have analysed your skills, try to record some evidence to support your evaluation.   .

Obtaining a Distinction grade

To obtain a *Distinction*, you must make realistic suggestions for improving your communication skills. One way to do this might be to design an action plan (see Figure 1.56).

Codes of practice and charters
Obtaining a Pass grade

To obtain a *Pass* grade, you must identify and describe codes of practice or charters used within the care settings you report on.

Obtaining a Merit grade

To obtain a *Merit* grade, you must explain how codes of practice and charters help to protect the users of services. You must explain that codes of practice and charters can provide definitions of good practice and can outline ways to protect people's rights. They are a measure of whether a service is providing good-quality care. If clients are not receiving a good-quality service, then charters and codes can help people to assert their rights and to make complaints.

You should obtain a full copy of the code of practice – perhaps from a library or from the organisation's web site. Pick out some examples in the code which you think provide clients with rights. Say what these rights are in your own words. How far does the code provide measurable standards or help people to understand their rights?

Codes of practice can also help managers to design policies and procedures that help staff provide a good service. If you interview senior care staff about the work people do in their organisations, you could also ask them if the value base, codes of practice or charters are used in staff training or staff supervision sessions. You could explain in your notes that, when staff work to improve the service they give, this will help to protect the clients. You could also explain that definitions of good practice can help professionals to think about the quality of their own personal practice. You could similarly ask staff about complaints procedures and about the ways the codes have influenced how these procedures are handled.

Obtaining a Distinction grade

To obtain a *Distinction*, you must evaluate the effectiveness of codes of practice and charters in upholding the broad principles of the care value base. This involves two tasks. First, you must show how different codes or charters include within their statements the principles of valuing diversity, clients' rights and confidentiality. You could discuss various codes with a friend and, together, try to work out what rights and what statements about confidentiality, equality and diversity the code includes. You will then have to write your own report on the code or charter. You could give your report the title: 'An analysis of the code (or charter) and its values'.

The second task is to find out just how seriously people use codes of practice or charters in real care settings. When you go on visits or on placements, ask the staff about values and codes of practice. You may find that some care settings give clients leaflets about their rights and offer training to their staff about rights and equality. They may also have complaints procedures that clearly explain these rights in relation to the codes or charters. If this is the case you can argue that codes and charters have a real effect on improving the quality of care services. On the other hand, you may come across care settings where values, codes and charters seem not to be understood. If you do, you could argue that theoretical ideas about rights do not always influence practice.

Try to work out why some care settings are better than others when it comes to rights and values. You could link this with the work you did on work roles and with the questions you asked staff for that task.

Unit I Test

1 What name is used to describe a service that has been set up because Parliament has passed a law requiring that service to be provided?

2 List three of the responsibilities of the new Health Authorities.

3 Which of the following definitions describes a 'mixed economy of care'?

   a People paying for their own care.
   b A mixture of provision through statutory, private and voluntary organisation.
   c People are means-tested before they can receive services from local social services departments or the NHS.

4 Describe briefly three different early years settings.

5 Describe the difference between the words 'direct' and 'indirect' when these words are used to describe jobs involved in the provision of care.

6 List three skills a nursery nurse should have.

7 At what ages can children receive early years services?

8 Explain what values are and why they are important in care work.

9 Explain two ideas for practical ways of valuing diversity in others.

10 Describe two general rights which clients might expect in a health or care setting.

11 Why are codes of practice and charters needed in care work?

12 Why are communication skills of great importance in care work?

13 What does 'non-verbal communication' mean?

14 How is listening different from just hearing what someone says?

UNIT I ASSESSMENT

Promoting health and well-being

This Unit covers the knowledge you will need in order to meet the assessment requirements for Unit 2. It is written in four sections:

Section one looks at definitions of health and well-being and how the health needs of different age groups differ. Section two explores the factors that affect health and well-being and the risks to health. Section three examines ways of providing health promotion information to support a health plan. Finally, section four explores indicators of good health. These are the actual physical measurements that can be done on the body.

Advice and ideas for meeting the assessment requirements for the unit and achieving Merit and Distinction grades are at the end of the Unit.

Also at the end of the Unit is a quick test to check your understanding.

Defining health and well-being

When we meet people we have not seen for some time, we usually ask how they are, and we would be quite surprised if they replied with full information about the state of their health – most of the responses we get are usually fairly simple and often inaccurate, such as 'fine' or 'not so bad'. Rarely do people tell us about details of their health or well-being.

Health and well-being are difficult things to understand or explain. Therefore the first part of this unit tries to provide clear explanations of the terms. It then goes on to explore the health and well-being of different groups of people. For example, to adolescents and young adults, being healthy might mean taking regular exercise by joining an aerobics group or playing football. However, this would not be a feature of the healthy lifestyle of an average 80-year-old person. To such a person, being healthy would more likely involve being able to do the tasks associated with independent daily living, such as shopping.

All people are unique and everyone has different health needs, but there are some things that affect everyone's health, such as what we eat and drink,

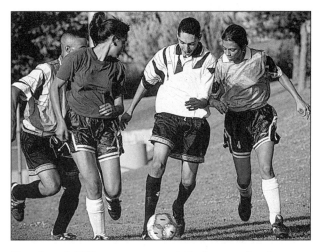

People of different ages get their exercise in different ways – young people often play sports such as football

where we live and the different incomes we have. These are the common factors that affect health, and these common factors are explored in greater detail later in this section.

Some people choose to do things that can be harmful to their health, such as smoking or taking too many legal or illegal drugs. Others choose not to do the things that are important to health, such as not wearing the correct protective clothing at work or not taking the right amount of exercise. This unit studies how these choices affect people's health and what people might be able to do to lessen their health risks.

This unit also explores ways to provide information to people to help them improve their general health, such as healthy eating leaflets and guidance on stopping smoking. Assessment tasks for this unit require you to investigate how to measure some aspects of people's physical health, to produce health targets for an individual (or group of people) and to understand how to involve them in improving their own health.

What is meant by health and well-being?

Health and well-being mean different things to different people; hence any definition has to involve everyone, which makes defining these terms difficult. The World Health Organisation has produced a definition of health which many people use: 'Health is a status of complete physical, mental, and social well-being and not merely the absence of disease and infirmity'. This definition was written in 1946 and has since been criticised on a number of points:

- The use of the word *complete* is seen by many people as being unrealistic (who can say he or she has 'complete mental well-being', for instance?).

- The use of the word *status* might imply that health does not change and that people do not change – that health is a level we reach and maintain. Clearly, this cannot be right: life is for ever changing.

- The definition implies that experts define our health but each individual may define his or her own health differently.

However, for all these criticisms, the World Health Organisation definition was a starting point to get people thinking about what health meant to them. Modern definitions of health emphasise health as the foundation from which people achieve all they are capable of – to enable them to satisfy their needs and realise their hopes; and to enable them to achieve quality in their lives. There is, and will continue to be, much discussion on the definition of health.

One thing most people agree with is that health is not just absence of illness or infirmity. It contains positive concepts about the physical, social, intellectual and emotional aspects of our lives (some might also include our spiritual needs).

Perhaps dividing the concept of health into these different aspects could be considered to be artificial, but it is useful for study purposes. However, it is important that we remember to consider people as whole human beings (this is called the holistic approach). The holistic approach is also known as PIES (and this might help us remember the four different aspects of health):

Physical
Intellectual
Emotional
Social

(see Figure 2.1).

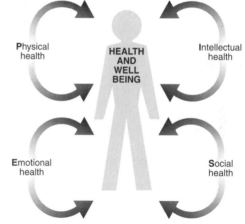

Figure 2.1   **PIES: the holistic approach to health**

Physical aspects of health

These aspects concern the physical functioning of the human body: sufficient food of the right types and proportions, clean drinking water, warmth provided by heating and clothing, having the right amount of sleep and rest and exercising regularly, etc. Illness and infirmity would also come in this category.

Social aspects of health

These include the ability to form good relationships with other people and the ability to maintain these relationships. Can people who live alone and avoid the company of others have good health? Using some definitions of health, the answer might be 'no'!

Intellectual aspects of health

These include the ability to think clearly and in an organised way. This does not mean that everyone should be trying to obtain academic qualifications although, for some people, this could be a feature of their health as they would be trying to achieve their own personal ambitions.

Emotional aspects of health

These include people's abilities to recognise emotions, such as grief, excitement, fear, joy etc., and to express these emotions appropriately. It also means being able to cope with stress, worry and depression (sadness) when these occur in our lives. Having emotional health does *not* mean *not* expressing your emotions!

Physical, social, intellectual and emotional are the aspects of health you need to consider in your health plan.

Different people and groups of people

For the purposes of study, people are often grouped into age ranges; they may also be grouped by other categories, such as vegetarians, smokers and people with learning disabilities.

The age ranges most commonly used are as follows:

- Infants (0–2 years, 11 months)
- Young children (3–9 years).
- Adolescents (10–18 years).
- Adults (19–65 years).
- Elderly people (over 65 years).

The physical, social, intellectual and emotional aspects of health we have just discussed will be very different for each of these age groups.

Try it out

Jade is 2 years old. She goes to a morning playgroup three times a week. Sarah, her mother, is a single parent on benefit. They live on their own in a two-room flat on the fourth floor of an old house, which is difficult to heat. There is no garden and the house is situated on a busy road. After paying her rent and buying food, Sarah has not much money left, so she buys most of her clothing in charity shops.

Complete the chart in Figure 2.2. Try to imagine Jade's and Sarah's situations: you can be very imaginative about this. Examples are provided for each aspect to guide you.

Factors affecting health and well-being

Many factors affect our health and well-being. Some of these factors affect certain people only but some are common to us all. In this section we look at those factors that affect all of us.

Diet

Diet is our pattern of eating. Sometimes a person's diet may not be adequate to keep that person's body in a healthy condition. This is often known as malnutrition. Malnutrition may be caused by:

1   *Not having enough food.* We often see this in undeveloped countries when there is a drought or famine. But it can also happen in countries like the UK: for example, old people living alone who are unable to afford or to cook food.

2   *Eating the wrong types of food.* Some people may only eat one type of food, for example, chips and buns. This means the body is not getting all the nutrients it needs.

3   *Eating too much refined food.* Refined foods are ones that have been processed to remove texture or taste. Examples are white sugar and white sliced bread. Eating too much of

Different aspects of health	Aspects of Jade's health	Aspects of Sarah's health
Physical	Jade is vulnerable to colds and chest infections, probably as a result of the cold, slightly damp conditions in her home.	
Social		Sarah cannot afford to socialise; she would have to pay for a child minder. On the mornings when Jade is at playgroup Sarah does the washing, ironing and tidying up. Occasionally, she meets a friend while shopping, but doesn't stay long with her. Sarah is lonely for adult company.
Emotional		Sarah is afraid that Jade might be taken into care if she went to work. She suffers from low spirits most of the time. She is short of money and cannot afford treats. Her previous partner has no interest in Jade. He left her when Sarah became pregnant. She feels unable to trust anybody else.
Intellectual	Jade is getting the chance to play with water and sand at playgroup, but her vocabulary seems more limited than the other 3 year-olds. She will need more stimulation to be able to cope with school life in 18 months' time. She has some favourite soft toys from the charity shop.	

Figure 2.2 Jade and Sarah

these foods can cause digestive disorders, diabetes and tooth decay.

4 *Eating far too much food.* If a person eats more food than his or her body needs, then the excess is laid down as fat under the skin and around the internal organs. This puts a great strain on the whole body and can lead to heart disease and other serious illnesses.

Consuming the right diet for our lifestyles is important for our health, and this is often called eating a **balanced diet**. A balanced diet is one that contains the correct nutrients in the correct proportions for healthy living. So how do we know what is appropriate for us?

The nutrients our bodies need fall into five main groups, with two additional requirements. These are carbohydrates (starches and sugars), proteins, fats, vitamins and mineral salts (and the additional requirements are water and fibre) (see Figure 2.3).

Figure 2.3   The nutrients our bodies need

Carbohydrates

Carbohydrates are the body's main source of energy. Complex carbohydrates, such as the starch in bread, rice and pasta, have to be broken down by enzymes in the digestive system; these are better for health than the refined sugars in sweets, soft drinks or sugar-containing foods. This is because sugar gives our bodies a quick boost of energy that falls rapidly, whereas complex carbohydrates provide our bodies with a slow build-up of energy that is sustained over a longer period.

Refined sugar also increases our chances of tooth decay and may play a part in causing diabetes. As complex carbohydrates usually contain fibre and certain vitamins and mineral salts, they can also help provide us with these nutrients.

Our diet should consist of 60% carbohydrates, mostly in the complex forms described above. From every gramme of carbohydrate we absorb into our bodies, we obtain 17 kJ (kilojoules) of energy.

Fat

Energy is also supplied by fat, but there is a danger here. Every gramme of fat we absorb gives our bodies 35 kJ of energy – twice as much as carbohydrates, but with more dangers attached

to it, so only 20% of our diet should be composed of fats and less if possible.

As well as giving us energy, fat also helps to:

- store the fat-soluble vitamins A, D, E and K
- protect the body's vital organs
- provide us with a long-term energy store
- provide us with the raw materials we need for making certain hormones
- provide us with the raw materials we need to make new cell membranes.

Hence some fat is essential if the body is to function properly. In Western societies, far too much fat is consumed and this can lead to heart and circulatory problems, such as heart attacks and strokes and also to muscular and joint disorders through carrying too much weight.

Proteins

Our diet should contain 20% protein as our bodies need this for the formation, growth and repair of cell structures. Some of the essential chemicals in our bodies are also proteins, such as enzymes, some hormones, haemoglobin (which is present in red blood cells and which carries oxygen), and blood-clotting substances and so on.

Vitamins

Vitamins act on the body in complex ways, and it is sufficient for our purposes just to be aware that they are essential to a healthy diet. They are only required in very small amounts and, if a person eats plenty of fresh fruit and vegetables, wholemeal bread, dairy products and cereals, he or she will take in sufficient quantities of these essential materials. An individual who eats only burgers and chips, chocolate bars and other manufactured products may have vitamin deficiencies.

Mineral salts

Again these act in complex ways and are required in only small amounts. They are supplied by fresh fruits and vegetables, red meat and dairy products. The two main mineral salts (which are required in larger quantities but still relatively small quantities when compared with proteins, fats and carbohydrates) are calcium for bone and teeth formation and iron – an essential component of haemoglobin.

Fibre

Fibre is the collective word for all the plant cell-walls we eat in our diet. Some people call fibre roughage, bran or cellulose but it is still the same material. Although it does not provide us with raw materials or energy, fibre has several important roles:

* It provides bulk in our food. It fills us up and makes us feel less hungry. Therefore in one sense it can be said to slim the body.

* It stimulates the muscular control of our bowels, thus preventing constipation.

* It helps to prevent diseases of the bowel, such as bowel cancer.

Fruit, vegetables, cereals and wholemeal products provide us with enough daily fibre.

Water

Tea, coffee and soft drinks can all be thought of as water because water is the main ingredient of all drinks. Even milk is mainly water.

Water is essential for life: it is the main component of our bodies – it makes our blood flow, gets rid of waste substances in urine, keeps our body cells moist, cools our bodies and dissolves oxygen and carbon dioxide and so on. We should drink around 3 litres of water every day.

Healthy eating

Once we know which foods provide each of the essential nutrients, we can plan a healthy diet.

In 1983 the National Advisory Committee for Nutrition Education (NACNE) produced five dietary goals to follow when planning meals. These goals were also recommended by the Committee on Medical Aspects of Food Policy (COMA):

1 Reduce our overall fat intake, but when we do eat fat make sure it is polyunsaturated, not saturated.

Figure 2.4 Dietary goals and health risks

Goal	Health risk	Change from	To
Eat less fat	High cholesterol Heart disease Obesity	Animal fats e.g. lard	Vegetable oil, e.g. corn
Eat less sugar	Tooth decay Obesity	Sweet puddings	Fresh fruit
Eat less salt	High blood pressure	Seasoning with salt	Using herbs or spices
Eat more fibre	Constipation Bowel cancer	White bread	Wholegrain bread
Drink less alcohol	Liver damage Stomach disorders	Alcoholic drinks	Low-alcohol drinks

2   Eat less salt.
3   Reduce our intake of sugar.
4   Eat more fibre.
5   Drink less alcohol.

Figure 2.4 shows the health risks if we do not follow these goals. The table also makes some suggestions about changing to a healthier diet.

Energy needs

The amount of energy needed by individuals is linked to their levels of activity: although each of us requires a different amount, there are general recommendations for every age group. It is important to balance our food intake to match our energy needs. Otherwise:

1   too little exercise + too much food = weight gain

2   too much exercise + too little food = weight loss.

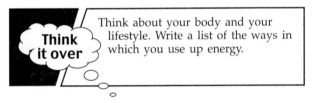

Think it over

Think about your body and your lifestyle. Write a list of the ways in which you use up energy.

1   **Basal metabolic rate** is the amount of energy required for your body to function when lying down, still and warm. It is lower for women than men because women tend to have smaller body masses. Any movement increases the number of kilojoules needed.

2   **Occupation** – different jobs require different levels of energy output and therefore different amounts of kilojoules are needed to sustain the people who do these jobs. Occupations are classified into groups:

   a   Sedentary – office workers, teachers, pilots, shop workers.
   b   Moderately active – postmen/women, nursery assistants, care assistants, hospital porters.
   c   Very active – miners, farm labourers, builders.

3   **Activity outside work** – the amount of exercise you take affects energy needs. Here are some examples of the energy use of different types of exercise:

	Average estimated kJ per hour
Sitting (watching TV)	400
Standing	425
Tennis	1645
Cycling	1900
Swimming	2500
Household tasks	950

4   **State of the body** – certain conditions, such as pregnancy and breast feeding (lactation), require an increase in energy intake to cope with the extra demands placed on the body.

5   **Age** – young children require more energy for their body size than adults as they are growing rapidly and also tend to be active all the time. On the other hand, ageing people require less energy as activity levels often slow down along with the general slowing down of the body processes.

Which foods provide energy?

All food provides some energy, but the amount per 100 g depends on the nutrient content of the food. Energy comes from four sources:

·   protein – 17 kJ/g
·   fat – 35 kJ/g
·   carbohydrate – 17 kJ/g
·   alcohol – 30 kJ/g.

Most foods are a combination of nutrients. The energy values of common foods are shown in Figure 2.5.

Figure 2.5 Some common foods and their energy values

Food	kJ per 100 g
Whole milk	274
White bread	1068
Butter	3006
Sugar	1680
Roast beef	950
Cod (steamed)	321
Apples	197
Cabbage	66
Crisps	2222
Chips	1028
Boiled potatoes	339
Sweet biscuits	1819

As can be seen from this table, a balance of input and output is complicated by the kilojoule values of food. A person's choice of foods can affect whether he or she achieves the right balance. An inactive person on a high-fat diet of chips, fried food, cakes, etc., would soon eat more than his or her energy needs. Excess calories taken into the body are stored as fat in the adipose layer under the skin which can lead to obesity.

Do all people need the same nutrients?

Everyone needs a balanced diet which contains all the nutrients. However, some groups have particular needs because of their life stage.

Children

Here are some tips for feeding children:

- This is a time of rapid growth so they need plenty of protein, vitamin D and calcium to develop strong bones.

- They also need fluoride to ensure strong enamel on their teeth to protect from decay, and iron for red blood cells.

- Milk is important, so if children do not like to drink it, give them plenty of milk in food.

- Children have small appetites, so give small portions and think about different ways to serve food attractively, for example, making faces in food might encourage a child to eat.

- Do not encourage children to eat sweets and snacks between meals as they will fill up on these and lose their appetite at meal times, which results in an unbalanced diet.

- Do not encourage the eating of sweet food between meals as this can contribute to tooth decay and obesity.

This advice continues right through until adolescence.

Pregnancy: 'eating for two'

It is essential that a pregnant woman eats a healthy balanced diet to ensure the health of both herself and her baby. Research has shown that a healthy diet is also vital before conception to help prevent foetal disorders and to ensure the woman's body is in the best condition to cope with the demands of pregnancy.

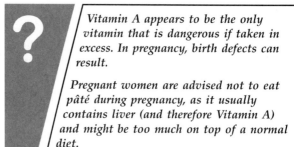

Vitamin A appears to be the only vitamin that is dangerous if taken in excess. In pregnancy, birth defects can result.

Pregnant women are advised not to eat pâté during pregnancy, as it usually contains liver (and therefore Vitamin A) and might be too much on top of a normal diet.

It is a myth that a pregnant woman should eat for two; this only leads to extra weight gain which may be difficult to lose after the birth. However, the intake of some nutrients does need to increase to meet the needs of the growing foetus. If the diet is lacking in any required nutrient, the body adjusts to ensure the baby has priority and the woman may hence suffer.

During pregnancy energy requirements increase as do the needs for certain minerals and proteins.

Calcium is required for the development of the foetus's skeleton. If there is not enough calcium to meet this demand, this will be removed from the mother's bones, which will then soften and bend (a condition known as osteomalacia). To help absorb the calcium, a greater quantity of vitamin D is also needed.

Iron is essential to the foetus as it develops its own blood supply. The baby also needs to build up a store of iron for its first three months of life as milk, either breast or formula, contains little iron.

It is also important that the mother's haemoglobin levels remain high as blood can be lost in delivery and a good iron level can help speed recovery. Iron tablets are often prescribed to pregnant women as iron in the diet is not always readily absorbed. One traditional source of iron, liver, should be avoided as the high amounts of vitamin A in liver have been linked to spina bifida. However, iron tablets tend to cause constipation and so an increase in fibre in the diet to prevent this is also needed.

Increases in energy requirements should come from healthy sources, such as pasta and bread, not sugar and fats.

The dietary goals outlined above should be followed throughout pregnancy and, in particular, alcohol consumption should be reduced. This is because alcohol crosses the placenta and can be harmful to the baby. Often, however, when pregnant, a woman finds she no longer likes certain foods such as tea, coffee and alcohol (all foods which could damage the foetus), but has cravings for other foods such as red meat and tomatoes. It is often suggested that these cravings are a result of deficiencies in the diet and are the body's way of getting the nutrients needed.

Older people

- As activity slows, the amount of calories eaten should be reduced to prevent obesity.

- The digestive system often slows, so the food chosen needs to be easily digested (such as fish).

- Poor teeth may cause problems with eating, so softer, well cooked foods should be chosen.

- It is wrong to say that older people do not like, or need to avoid, spicy foods. Ageing can dull the taste buds so some older people may like spicy foods for their flavour.

- Diets should be high in calcium and vitamin D to help prevent decalcification – removal of calcium from the bones and teeth. A loss of calcium can also lead to osteoporosis, which results in weaker bones more prone to fractures and breaks.

- Protein is important to maintain and renew cells.

- Fibre levels need to be increased as the slowing of the digestive system, along with reduced mobility, may cause constipation.

- Iron is needed to prevent anaemia.

- The NACNE food goal recommendations (see pages 65–66) should be followed.

Social factors also play a part in an older person's quality of diet, especially if living alone. Research has shown that older people living on their own often do not eat properly because it is 'not worth the bother of cooking for one'. In cases where a partner has died, the remaining person may become disorientated while grieving, and so miss meals and not eat properly. This can also happen if a person begins to suffer memory loss.

Physical difficulties may affect diet. For example, lack of mobility may mean it is difficult for an older person to go to a supermarket where there is more choice of healthy foods and food is cheaper. Older people may be restricted to shopping close to home in a corner shop. Level of mobility may also affect an older person's ability to cook, and this can also affect the quality of diet. A person with arthritis may have difficulty preparing fresh vegetables and so may rely on frozen varieties, which may contain fewer nutrients.

Work, rest and play

A **healthy lifestyle** may be thought of as a **balanced lifestyle**, one which includes the right amounts of activity – work and recreation – and rest – inactivity and sleep. Each person is different and we all live happily on differing amounts of work and rest. As life changes a person's work and rest patterns change. Take for example, the lifestyle of many young students. Their course may be considered their 'work'; but they may also have a part-time job.

Work may take up five days per week and they possibly work some evenings at their jobs. Younger students may spend much of their time working. They relax by going out in the evenings after work and may survive on five hours' sleep a night. The younger student may be able to cope with this balance.

Another type of lifestyle is that of an older care assistant who may work an eight-hour shift each day for five days of the week, with the remainder of the time spent on leisure activities, sleep and socialising. This may represent a balance that meets the needs of the older person.

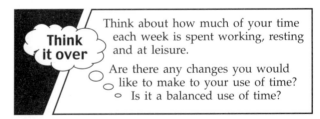

Think it over

Think about how much of your time each week is spent working, resting and at leisure.

Are there any changes you would like to make to your use of time? Is it a balanced use of time?

Why are sleep and rest important?

The human body is like a rechargeable battery. It cannot keep going without recharging itself. The body does this through sleep. During sleep the body is in a state of unconsciousness which allows the individual to cope with the activity of the day. If a person is not getting enough sleep, he or she is less able to cope with day-to-day life and is more prone to accidents and psychological problems, such as stress.

Non-physical activities

A large number of people enjoy non-physical activities that provide for their emotional, social and intellectual needs. For example, reading helps people unwind, particularly reading in bed before sleeping. It also provides intellectual stimulation and talking points when in the company of friends.

Sewing and knitting can be creative, useful and emotionally satisfying. Board games and quiz games are socially and intellectually enjoyable, while collecting stamps, coins, miniature cars, electric trains and other similar 'collectables' satisfies our emotional, and often intellectual, needs.

Many people with fairly ordinary jobs are amateur star performers in music making, singing and amateur dramatics!

Try it out

With a partner, make a four-column chart like the one below. Write down in the first column all the leisure and recreational activities you can both think of (take 10 minutes to do this). Tick the appropriate columns for each activity, saying which need is satisfied by the activity. 'Reading' has been entered for you.

Activity	Emotional satisfaction	Intellectual satisfaction	Social satisfaction
Reading	✓	✓	✓

Another way the body recharges itself is through rest or inactivity. Doing very little physically, such as watching the television or reading, can also promote health for people who lead physically active lives.

Exercise and health

Taking exercise is an important part of keeping healthy, and there are many different and enjoyable ways to do so. A person can become fit by exercising about three times a week for 20 minutes. Exercise can range from walking to water-skiing, or from a gentle game of badminton to a hard workout in a gym.

Exercise should make use of the muscles but you should always warm up before any exercise, no matter how fit you are. You should also cool down as part of the routine.

Vigorous exercise can be fun!

Most forms of exercise can be taken at different paces and levels. It is important to make sure the pace and level are chosen to suit the fitness of the individual.

Most exercise is a combination of **anaerobic** exercise, which stretches muscles, and aerobic exercise, which works the heart and lungs.

The benefits of exercise

Apart from the effects it has on our physical health, regular exercise has many other benefits. It helps us feel good and can also make us more relaxed, confident and able to cope with the strains of life (see Figure 2.7).

Figure 2.6   The effectiveness of different forms of exercise

Exercise	Strength	Stamina	Suppleness	Kcal/min
Badminton	**	**	***	5–7
Cycling (hard)	***	****	**	7–10
Golf	*	*	**	2–5
Dancing (disco)	*	***	****	5–7
Ballroom dancing	*	*	***	2–5
Swimming (hard)	****	****	****	7–10
Walking briskly	*	**	*	5–7
Climbing stairs	**	***	*	7–10

*Fair **Good ***Very good ****Excellent

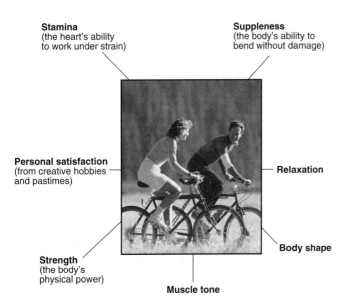

Figure 2.7   The benefits of exercise

Exercise can be a way for people to make new friends. It can also play a role in developing co-operative skills, especially in children.

The benefits of each form of exercise are often rated according to how much the exercise improves strength, stamina and suppleness (see Figure 2.6).

Environment

Environment includes an individual's immediate environment (such as his or her home, flat or place of residence), the individual's locality (such as an inner city, a leafy suburb or a rural community) or much wider regional, national or international environments. We must also include the environments of people who are homeless, of those in work and the play environments of children. The concept of 'environment' is hence very complex (see Figure 2.8).

The ideal environment for everyone would be in a land where there was no unemployment, no ill-health, no crime, no pollution, no poverty, the best housing, the best diet, the best education and total support for each other socially and emotionally. In reality, this is unlikely ever to happen.

Our environment can affect our growth and development, and it can afffect our potential. If we all lived in exactly the same environment, had the same illnesses and accidents, and ate the same diet, we would be likely to develop in a much more similar way than we really do. Our environment affects the opportunities we have in life, the attitudes we hold and the way we feel

Figure 2.8   How our environment can affect us

Try it out

Using flip charts and in small groups, brainstorm the possible ways in which an individual's health might be affected by his or her home environment. Here are some key words to get you started (you will be able to think of more):

location	overcrowding	solitary living
stairs	lighting	ventilation
damp	cooking facilities	sleeping arrangements
level (basement, high rise)	dirt	cleaning
noise	vulnerability	safety
sanitation	living accommodation	pets
garden/no garden	neighbours	heating

When you have exhausted your key words, put the charts up for the whole group to view and discuss. Next, take three 'post-its' each and, using three key words, write a sentence on each saying how the key word might affect someone's health.

For example: 'Vulnerability: an old person living in an inner-city flat might be very frightened of violent intruders – this would seriously affect his or her emotional and social health.'

about ourselves. We all have different experiences of life, partly because of where we live and whom we live with, and partly because of the situations we experience.

Look at the 'Try it out' above. You could repeat the same task for your own locality. Study the

annual reports published by your local Health Authority or public health or social services departments. These reports will give you valuable information. For example, if you live in an area that has certain industries, such as chemical works, steel plants or oil refineries, there may be health risks associated with these industries. The reports may contain advice or guidance about these risks (see Figure 2.9).

Social class

The term 'class' is one way to categorise people, depending on their income. For many years people's income and jobs were used by the Registrar General when measuring the UK's population in the ten-yearly Census. However, in

Serious chemical incidents, like major outbreaks, are rare but the concentration of chemical sites in the area means that co-ordinated planning to deal with spillages are vital...

The Health Authority's role is perhaps not as well known as the role of other agencies (Police, Fire and Ambulance, Health and Safety Executive, Environmental Health). However, as part of its remit to protect the health of the population in the area it does have important responsibilities. These are:

- to ensure that there are hospital facilities to treat people affected by toxic chemicals

- to provide medical advice to the public and to other health professionals, in liaison with the emergency services. In the event of a serious incident to ensure collection of appropriate samples from people affected in an incident and

- to determine the need for long term surveillance of those affected and if this is necessary, to ensure that appropriate surveillance is carried out.

The local hospital has recently reviewed the facilities in the Accident and Emergency Department for dealing with chemically contaminated people and new decontamination facilities are being designed as a result of this review.

This report also mentions an outbreak of gastro-intestinal disease which affected 50 people. It was thought to have been associated with drinking water – another environmental factor that affects people's health.

Figure 2.9 Extract from the Wirral Public Health Report 1998, *Building Partnerships for Better Health*

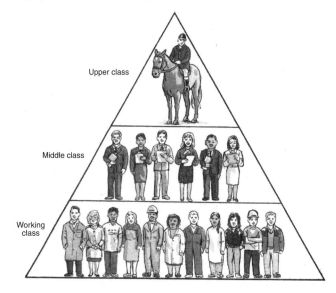

Figure 2.10 Social class

Figure 2.11

Social classifications expected to be used in the 2001 census	
1.1	Employers and managers in larger organisations, for example company directors.
1.2	Higher professionals, for example doctors, solicitors, teachers.
2	Lower managerial and professional occupations, for example nurses, journalists.
3	Intermediate occupations, for example clerks, secretaries.
4	Small employers and own account workers, for example taxi drivers, painters and decorators.
5	Lower supervisory, craft and related occupations, for example plumbers, train drivers.
6	Semi-routine occupations, for example shop assistants, hairdressers.
7	Routine occupations, for example cleaners, refuse collectors.

Those who are long-term unemployed form a final, eighth group.

December 1998, the National Statistics Office drew up a new method of classifying the population, and six **socioeconomic** classes first drawn up in 1911 were replaced by seven others (see Figure 2.11). People's socioeconomic status is now not just based on people's earnings but on the conditions of their employment (such things as job security, sick pay, pensions and the amount of control individuals have over their workloads). (See Unit 3 for details about income and wealth.)

Why should people's social class affect their health and well-being? Why should it matter how we measure social class? From the discussion of social class we have just had, these questions might come into our minds. But when we look at the population when it is categorised like this we find differences in the statistics about the amount of disease (morbidity) and early death (mortality) among the classes. For both males and females we find that, in over 80% of diseases, there is a steady rise in disease from social class 1 to the lower classes (see Figure 2.11). People at the bottom of the table and those who have been unemployed for a long time have higher amounts of heart and circulation problems, ulcers, mental illnesses, certain cancers, arthritis and many more illnesses. Such people also have a worse

likelihood of survival of certain cancers than people in the top classes.

It may also be the case that working-class areas of the country tend to have fewer (and worse) facilities for health care than other areas. People in the lower classes also tend to smoke and drink more than people in class 1 and, consequently, suffer more from smoking-related illnesses and alcohol problems. We could also perhaps assume that people from class 1 can afford leaner cuts of meat than people in other classes, and that they can easily afford balanced diets. Similarly, people with a good income may also have the money, time and education to take advantage of health clubs, exercise, sport and health information.

We could perhaps conclude from all this that social class has a serious effect on people's health and well-being.

Employment

A government health policy document called *Health of the Nation* states that 'people in manual groups are, for example, more likely to smoke and eat diets containing less Vitamin C and beta-carotene [a substance the body can convert to vitamin A]. There is also a higher proportion of heavy drinkers in manual than non-manual groups (though on the other hand there is also a higher proportion of people who never drink or who drink only lightly and infrequently). There is also evidence of lower take-up of preventive health services (e.g. immunisation, child health surveillance) in the most vulnerable groups.

> **Think it over**
>
> Why do you suppose the information in this document could be true? Try to give reasons for the three main points (smoking, diet and drinking) mentioned in the document. Could these be linked to the pressures and restrictions people in manual work suffer from?

Our work has a profound effect on our health and well-being: it provides our income, which, in turn, influences our standard of living. It also has far-reaching effects on us emotionally and mentally and can affect the 'speed' at which we live.

A person in a high-powered job will usually receive a salary that reflects the pressure he or she is under. However, such a person may find that, although he or she can afford a magnificent home, he or she never has the time to be there. His or her health and mental state may similarly be threatened because of the pressure he or she is under.

People in very low-paid jobs are equally under pressure though for different reasons. Trying to make ends meet and juggling the household bills are extremely stressful when someone is on a limited income. To have no employment at all has similar effects. No work means very little money coming in and a restricted lifestyle. In some areas of the UK unemployment figures are so high that it is very difficult for people to get jobs. Unemployment has a profound effect on self-esteem and motivation: what is the point of trying to get GCSEs if there are no jobs to go after?

Unemployment affects the way we treat other people. We may think that we cannot, or have no right to, approach others for help. It also affects the treatment that we receive from others, the services we are entitled to, and our attitudes to life. Finally, many people work simply for the money rather than for the satisfaction they get from their jobs. However, it could be argued that the more satisfaction a job gives us, the less stress we will be under. On the other hand, work itself is not without its problems, as we all know. And it perhaps comes as no surprise that there are far

more employment-related accidents among the working classes than among the middle and professional classes. Many people are at risk of falls, cave-ins, 'dust' that can affect the respiratory system, injury to the eyes, etc., as a consequence of the work they do. The people who work in the emergency services (for example, the police, ambulance staff and firemen and women) have jobs that are dangerous in themselves but they must also deal with stressful incidents that may leave them depressed and anxiety-ridden. Research suggests that teachers, nurses and doctors also have very stressful occupations and that these people can be subjected to violent attacks from the people they come into contact with.

People who work in offices can develop repetitive strain injury, neck and back problems from poorly designed furniture, and depression and anxiety as a result of work overload and pressure. Similarly, we all might suffer emotional, social or physical problems that arise from racial, sexual, cultural or age discrimination.

Housing

Our income inevitably affects where we are able to live, and how we can afford to live there. For example, people on low incomes are more likely to rent rather than to buy and if we do not have regular work or a regular income, it is unlikely that banks or building societies will lend us the money for a mortgage.

All types of work can put people under stress

Talk it over

With your friends, discuss which parts of the area you live in are most expensive and which the least. What are the reasons for this?

You could consider the facilities within each area, the amount of space between dwellings and the proximity of busy roads or heavy traffic.

Where we live and the type of dwelling we live in affect our health. If our home is in a badly maintained high rise in the inner city, with no access to safe play for our children, we are going to be under greater stress than someone living in more open conditions. Everyone lives with some stress but not everyone has the option or the money to escape for a while to relax. Stress can lead to ill health as a result of low income or poor housing; on the other hand, if we have a regular income and a secure job, we are more likely to be able to afford a better standard of living and the good health that accompanies this.

Income

Income is not just the amount of money we earn; it also has a great effect on our lives. If we have a high income we are less likely to worry about being able to pay the rent or feed our children. If we have a low income, we are less likely to worry about keeping up with the latest fashions or buying a new sports car. According to our incomes, different things become more or less important to us.

Education

Learning is something we do from birth, yet we only gain formal qualifications via the education we receive at school or college. The opportunities for education are not the same for everyone. By law, a child is entitled to education between the ages of 5 and 16 years but some children start and leave school earlier than others. All sorts of factors influence the amount of education a person receives (see Figure 2.12).

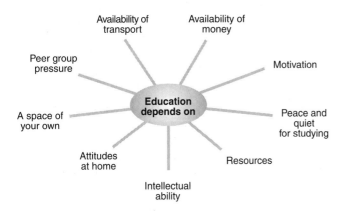

Figure 2.12   The factors that affect our education

Education can affect people in different ways. Sometimes our education turns us against those things our upbringing told us were right and proper – be it our political views, our tastes for music, or simply those things that constitute 'a good square meal'. Although diet may seem trivial when put alongside politics, culture etc., if we think about what we eat it is very difficult to divorce our eating habits from our other attitudes about life – and it is our education (or lack of education) that has guided us in our eating habits. What we learn (or fail to learn) tells us what constitutes 'proper' food.

To confuse things even further, health messages have changed over the years. Dairy products were once considered to be very good for us but now the experts are saying that it is better to drink semi-skimmed milk. Potatoes and bread were once considered fattening, but now we are told to eat them – and to cut down on the butter instead! Red meat (i.e. beef, lamb and pork) was also considered to be an essential part of weekend meals, provided people could afford to buy it, but now healthy eating advice is not to eat too much red meat, but to eat more white meat – chicken and fish.

So how do we find out what is *supposed* to be good for us? One way is to read leaflets.

Carry out a survey, with permission, of shoppers in a local supermarket which supplies free information on healthy eating. Count the number of shoppers emerging from the cash tills and those who pick up or even look at the free information provided.

You could further extend this activity, with a simple questionnaire to shoppers asking them when they last looked at or picked up leaflets, then whether they read them.

How individuals can control the factors that affect their health and well-being

Many of the factors we have studied cannot be easily altered: issues such as income, employment, housing and social class. However, we can change some of the factors that affect our health and well-being, such as lack of exercise, diet, smoking, alcohol consumption, sexual behaviour and unsafe practices in the workplace.

It is not possible, however, in some situations to tell whether an individual has control or not and, in some instances, the individual may not want to believe he or she has control. A good example is education. There are many people who have not achieved their full potential educationally, but who were quite capable of doing so: they just did not want to challenge themselves.

Life choices and life chances

Some people say that everyone has a choice about his or her lifestyle. We can choose to exercise or be lazy; we can choose to follow a healthy diet or not; we can choose to practise safe sex; and we can choose not to take drugs. This all seems fine until we think about the ways poverty and stress can influence people.

If we live in a stressful neighbourhood or are under stress because we are unemployed we might not be able to choose our lifestyles as easily as someone who has a more comfortable life. Similarly, if we have to work long hours we may not easily be able to find the time to exercise. If we are depressed we may not care about the rules of safe sex, or we may feel the urge to take drugs. Hence people may *not* all have the same life chances.

Talk it over

In a group, discuss how you think young people's life chances are affected in the area where you live.

Is everyone able to shop easily, can everyone use the area's public and private facilities, and is everyone able to go out in the evenings?

In 1995, about a fifth of Britain's population and a quarter of Britain's children were considered to be living in poverty and, as we have already noted, poverty is one of the main influences on our life choices and life chances. There are different ways of measuring what it is to be poor. One measure is to use the amount of money paid to people receiving Income Support. This level of income is often called the poverty line.

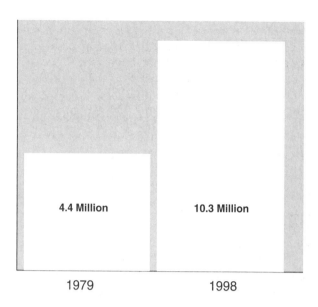

4.4 Million   10.3 Million

1979   1998

Figure 2.13 Poverty in Britain

The key groups of people who have to live on or below the poverty line include:

* one-parent families

* elderly people

* single-earner, unskilled couples (where only one person works in an unskilled job)

* people who are unemployed

* people who are sick or disabled.

In 1998 an estimated 10.3 million people in Britain lived on or below this poverty line; in 1979, however, only 4.4 million people were estimated to be living in poverty (see Figure 2.13). The number of people who can be considered to be poor increased during the 1990s and may continue to increase in the future.

People who are poor may have enough money for food, for some clothes and for heating, but poverty means there is little money for the interesting purchases that make for exciting lifestyles: people who depend on benefits have limited life choices.

The latest clothes, comfortable and reliable cars, the latest electronic equipment, digital TV and so on may not be possible for people on a low income. People with little money have to restrict what they can buy when they visit a supermarket or shopping centre.

Many lifestyles are not possible for people in poverty. Belonging to a sports club is not possible if you can't afford the membership fees, the equipment and so on. Even jogging isn't possible if you feel your neighbourhood isn't safe to go out in.

Children living in poverty may have limited life choices and limited life chances to develop their full social, emotional and intellectual potential.

Risks to health
Substance abuse

People may use drugs or other substances in a way that feels pleasurable but that may be harmful to their health. For example glue is meant to stick things together, not to be inhaled. Many substances can be misused and these range from, for example, too much coffee causing nervous tension, to an individual who is addicted to 'crack' cocaine (see Figure 2.14). The word 'drug' also covers nicotine and alcohol, both of which are legal in the UK. Choosing to use any drug has an effect on our bodily functions.

Misuse of drugs
All kinds of drugs are available and they may be obtained in three main ways:

* The first way is from a doctor, via a prescription made up by the chemist. These are known as **prescribed drugs** and are part of a treatment given to combat an illness. Prescribed drugs are supplied with instructions and a list of side-effects you should be aware of.

* Some drugs are sold to the public by chemists or supermarkets. These are known as **over-the-counter drugs**. Supermarkets and other shops only sell paracetamol and similar drugs in small quantities in order to try and limit their misuse.

Figure 2.14   Substance abuse can take many forms

* It is illegal to possess **controlled drugs** except in certain special circumstances. These are often the types of drugs that can lead to addiction or that have dangerous side-effects if misused. Examples of controlled drugs are cannabis or cocaine.

Drugs misuse can have profound effects on us (see Figure 2.16). And the effects listed in the table are only the tip of the iceberg. Figure 2.17 analyses some of the most commonly misused drugs.

Solvent abuse
Solvents are substances used in the manufacture

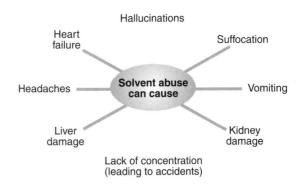

Figure 2.15   The effects of solvent abuse

Figure 2.16   The effects of misusing drugs

Psychological	Physical	Social
Depression	Heart problems	Crime
Paranoia (thinking people are against you)	Risk of HIV	Homelessness
Psychosis (total mental confusion)	Risk of hepatitis B/C	Employment problems

Figure 2.17 Chart to show effects and risks of some commonly misused drugs

Misused drug	Appearance and use	Effects of use	Possible risks to health
Cannabis or hash, grass, marijuana, Black Leb, rocky, weed	Like dried herbs, a dark brown block or sticky and treacle-like Usually smoked but sometimes eaten	Feeling of sickness, hunger or worry More alert and talkative Imagines things (hallucinations)	Bronchitis and damage to lungs Raised pulse rate and blood pressure Inactivity and loss of memory Mental illness
LSD or acid, trips, tabs	Blotters and micro-dots that are swallowed	Greater self-awareness Disorientated in time and place Altered hearing, panic Depression and feeling that everyone and everything is against them (paranoia)	Never quite returning to previous normal state and needing more and more to achieve the same effects (tolerance) Flashbacks Anxiety Disorientation and depression
Heroin or H, Henry, smack	White or brown powder that is injected, sniffed up the nose or smoked	Feeling sleepy and coddled	HIV/AIDS and Hepatitis B when it is injected Thrombosis of veins or abscess at the injection sites Blood infection (septicaemia) Heart and lung disorders Can be fatal if impure
Ecstasy or E, xtc, M25s, lovedoves, Adam	Flat, round tablets that are swallowed	Confidence, calmness and alertness Thirst, anxiety Symptoms of heat stroke Sexual feelings	Nausea, headache and giddiness Raised body temperature with no sweating Muscular cramps Collapse Mental illness including paranoia
Cocaine, coke, snow or Charlie	White powder that is injected or sniffed	Anxiety, thirst and heat stroke symptoms	HIV/AIDS and Hepatitis B when it is injected Thrombosis of veins or abscess at the injection sites
Crack	Crystals that are smoked	Feel on top of the world, could do anything Panic, worry or hostility	Blood infection (septicaemia) Heart and lung disorders Addictive Raised body temperature with no sweating, muscular cramps Lack of appetite (anorexia)
Amphetamines or speed, sulph, whizz	White powder in tablets or screws of paper that is swallowed, sniffed or injected	Palpitations (increased force and rate of heart beat), weakness, hunger Lots of energy and confidence Depression and worry	HIV/AIDS and Hepatitis B when it is injected Raised blood pressure and risk of stroke Mental illness Tolerance develops
Solvents or glue, Evo, aerosols, petrol, lighter fluid	Various fluids or sprays that are sniffed	Heightened imagination, depression, happiness or sadness, hostility Fatigue, confusion Liver and kidney damage	Liver and kidney damage Increased risk of accidents during the abuse Heart failure, suffocation, vomiting/choking, death

of glue, lighter fuel, petrol and aerosols. People sniff or inhale these products to get 'high' on the solvents they contain. For some people the effect is rather like being drunk: it makes them feel sad, happy, sleepy or wobbly on their feet. For others the reaction may be different. They may lose their appetites, have headaches or feel sick, or feel confused or hallucinate. Solvent misuse can cause convulsions, coma or death, even the first time a person tries it. It is against the law in the UK for children to buy items that may be misused, for example, lighter fuel and certain glues.

CASE STUDY – Cassie and Mick

Cassie and Mick are both aged 15 years and have been friends for about three months. They spend their Friday and Saturday evenings at raves where Mick often supplies Cassie with an ecstasy tablet. Recently they are both finding that school is even more tiring and boring than usual, but the weekends are much better: the ecstasy they take gives them more energy and life seems to be much more fun.

Jen, Cassie's friend, is worried about the ecstasy Cassie takes. She is for ever nagging Cassie about the dangers of heat stroke and dehydration: apparently, you can drink too much liquid and flood your brain. Cassie thinks this is funny. She knows that if you drink just *one* pint of water an hour you're usually OK. Jen thinks Cassie will become addicted, but Cassie knows she won't. This is just a way of relaxing at the weekend. Anyway, it's not as if she buys drugs from some shady looking character lurking in a doorway somewhere – Mick gets them from his mate – and your friends wouldn't mess you up.

Sometimes it is difficult to 'come down' after a rave. Cassie finds she can't get to sleep, and she always wakes up feeling tired and depressed that she has to go back to school on Monday. One of Mick's friends has offered to get them some 'brown', which he says makes you sleep like a baby and wake up feeling great. Neither Mick nor Cassie are aware that 'brown' is one of the names used for heroin.

Questions

Discuss the above case study:

1 What short-term benefits are Mick and Cassie getting?

2 How dangerous do you think their habit is?

3 Should Jen interfere further?

4 What longer-term effects are in danger of arising?

5 Could Mick be charged with supplying Cassie with drugs?

6 Where do you think they are getting their money to support their recreational habits?

7 What could the effects be if 'brown' was to replace ecstasy?

We do not always listen to good advice

As using solvents can cause dizziness or make someone pass out, misusing them by a busy road, by water, near a railway line or on top of high buildings adds to the chance of serious injury (see Figure 2.15).

The misuse of drugs and solvents: overview

Developing a tolerance to any drug can mean that more is needed each time to get the same effect. This means increased costs and increased risks. Also, most drugs that are misused are not made under safe laboratory conditions. Some drugs are contaminated with other dangerous substances, and so the effects are unpredictable. Some drugs may be deliberately mixed with other substances and some could be far weaker or stronger than those previously experienced.

Alcohol

Any decisions we make that affect our health have both short and long-term effects. Deciding to drink alcohol can, in the short term, make us feel good. In the slightly longer term it could mean loss of self-control. In the even longer term constant overuse of alcohol could mean alcoholism or cirrhosis of the liver. Cirrhosis is the condition where the liver enlarges in an attempt to cope with the excess amounts of alcohol: it becomes inflamed and hardens. It

consequently stops working and the body is poisoned.

Some of the effects of alcohol are as follows:

◇ Alcohol slows down sections of the brain – abuse of alcohol can actually make your brain shrink!

◇ It causes weight gain – alcohol is very high in kilojoules.

◇ Alcohol weakens the immune system.

◇ Heavy drinking can affect sexual performance.

◇ Alcohol can give an initial 'high', followed by depression.

◇ It can become habit forming, and people can become dependent on it.

Tobacco

You will have noticed significant changes in social attitudes to smoking in the past few years. A very large number of workplaces and public places are now totally non-smoking areas or only permit smoking in certain restricted places. The hazards of smoking are now fairly well known as they have been well documented in the media and are printed on cigarette and other smoking material packaging. If you need to refresh your memory about these hazards, study Figure 2.18.

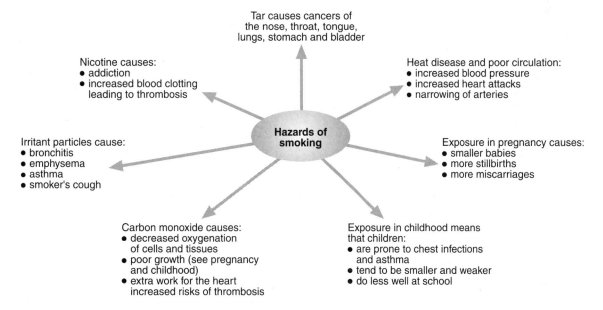

Figure 2.18   The hazards of smoking

Under the Health and Safety at Work Act 1974, employers have a duty to ensure the health, safety and welfare of their employees. More recently, European legislation has made it a requirement of employers that they must provide smoke-free rest areas and rest rooms. This requirement has been reinforced lately by reports about the risks to health from passive smoking. Passive smoking occurs when non-smokers inhale unfiltered smoke from the smokers around them. Such smoke has larger amounts of tar, nicotine and other irritants than that inhaled by the smoker.

Some non-smoking, well-known entertainers have died as a consequence of working for many years in smoky night-clubs and similar places. The foetuses of pregnant women are also passive smokers.

The following statistics about smoking have been compiled by the Royal College of Physicians:

◇ Smoking-induced illness accounts for 50 million lost working days each year.

◇ In England, 16 million working days are lost due to bronchitis, emphysema and asthma alone.

◇ Some 28% of people in paid employment would prefer it if their employers banned smoking altogether in their workplace.

Massive extra costs are incurred as a result of fire, refurbishment and redecoration, cleaning, drains on funds, health insurance, early retirement, smoking breaks – the list could go on and on! (See Figure 2.19 for advice on how to assist smokers to stop smoking.)

Diet

'You are what you eat'. Although this is an old saying, it is largely true. Our health is greatly affected by our diet and the way we use the energy food gives us. There are many benefits from eating the right sorts of food in the correct quantities. If you eat too much once in a while, it is unlikely you will come to harm, apart from feeling a little bloated. If you constantly over-eat, your body will start to store fat under your skin in a thick layer. More importantly, it will store the excess fat on your organs and inside your arteries. Both of these are dangerous to our health and could lead to possible heart disease in later life.

When people put on weight, they do so gradually and usually do not notice it happening. Suppose over a few years you put on six kilogrammes. Carrying that extra weight is the same as carrying a vacuum cleaner around with you wherever you go. Imagine how tiring that would be. If you are overweight the same strain is put on your heart, muscles and back.

Under-eating is also unhealthy. A common condition induced by under-eating is anaemia, which is caused by a lack of iron in the diet. Anaemia occurs when the concentration of

The following is a list of traditional ways to stop smoking. There are also many new therapies, which can be found from web sites about the risks of smoking.

● Change the habits you have acquired that encourage you to smoke (for example if you usually smoke after lunch, take a short walk instead).

● Cut down on the number of cigarettes smoked over a period of time rather than trying to stop suddenly.

● Use substitute nicotine gum or patches (with counselling support).

● Ask friends and family for their support.

● Use the money saved to buy a longed-for treat.

● Restrict your opportunities for smoking, such as one cigarette only in the evening.

● Change your brand of cigarettes to one which has a very low tar content.

You will find several leaflets about stopping or reducing smoking at your local health education unit, or from the Health Education Authority and the anti-smoking organisation, ASH.

Figure 2.19   Advice on how to stop smoking

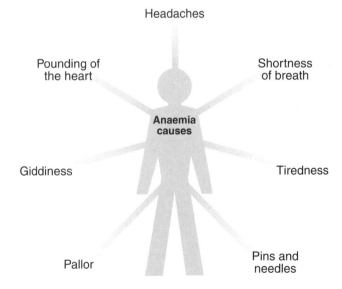

Figure 2.20   The effects of anaemia

haemoglobin in the blood falls and this prevents the oxygen in your blood from being carried around your body efficiently (see Figure 2.20).

People, who change their diet, for example, by becoming a vegetarian could be prone to anaemia. Another group who are susceptible to anaemia are teenage girls and young women, who are trying to alter or achieve their desired body shape. Because they cut down on iron-rich foods and generally eat less, they do not get the nutrients they need.

people are able to make. If you do not have enough money to buy the leanest cuts of meat, or the freshest fruit and vegetables, your diet is going to be less healthy than someone who can afford to buy these. The diets of people living 'on the breadline' are much worse than those with a higher income.

Suppose you have less than £50 a week to feed five of you: your main purpose in buying food would be to stop people from feeling hungry, rather than meeting all their nutritional needs. The easiest, fastest way to stop hunger is to eat

Weigh and measure yourself, and then see where you are on a standard height/weight chart. You will notice that the bands for each particular measurement are quite wide.

Why do you think this is?

Are you in the band you expected to be in?

Try to work out a week's *healthy* menus for five people with only £50 to spend. Remember, that's only £10 per person for the whole week. You may have to undertake some research to do this realistically. Work out main meals for each day and then draw up a list of the things you need (you can exclude those things most people have in their 'larders' – things like salt, flour, sugar, jam, oil, margarine etc.). Go to a supermarket and check prices against those items on your list.

Can you afford to buy all the things you have planned to eat? Are you tempted to 'cut corners' and dive into the freezer compartment for that cheap bumper pack of burgers? How frustrating do you find the whole experience?

Poverty and diet

Eating the right foods in the correct quantities is rather like putting petrol, oil and water in a car: it keeps you running and ensures all your parts are maintained in working order (see Figure 2.21). Poverty has a huge effect on the health choices

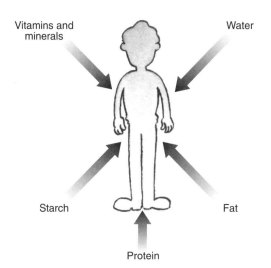
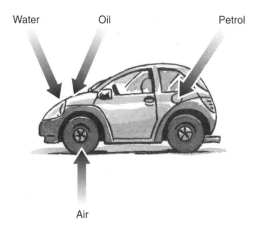

Figure 2.21   Just as a car needs petrol, we all need the correct food to keep our bodies in working order

high-fat carbohydrate foods: chip butties, tinned spaghetti on toast, deep-fried anything. Advice from the exerts about improving our diets by eating five helpings of fruit and vegetables a day is less easy to follow when you are living on a limited income. Alternatives have to be found.

Poverty can spiral people into ill-health. And once we enter this spiral, it is very difficult to break free of an inevitable descent into being unable to cope with the pressures of life (see Figure 2.22).

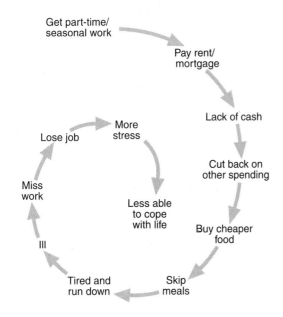

Figure 2.22   Poverty and diet: the vicious circle

Stress

Most people suffer from stress at some time in their lives, and a small amount of stress can be good for us: it makes our bodies respond more vigorously to meet the challenges of life. It is the grind of continual stress that is so harmful to us.

Think it over

How many people can you think of who work (or worked) in entertainment, particularly comedians, who have suffered from heart disease?

How many entertainment people can you think of who find sport, particularly golf, a way of coping with the stress of performing?

Try it out

There are many symptoms of stress. The following are but a few:

Anxiety	Sleeplessness	Tiredness
Heart disease	Diarrhoea	Poor sex life
Irritability	Short temperedness	Unhappiness
_____	_____	_____
_____	_____	_____

Try to add to this list.

Individuals or groups who suffer from stress will find that, eventually, their relationships will break down, they will become depressed and they may develop mental illnesses. They may even become violent or suicidal. Alternatively they may withdraw from the world and become anti-social. Either way people's health will suffer and this is why stress management training is now accepted as necessary to prevent people who suffer from stress from becoming ill. Stress management training helps find ways of minimising stress or ways to cope with stress.

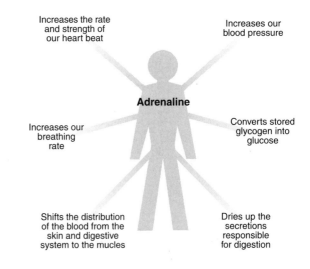

Figure 2.23   The effects of adrenaline

The way our bodies respond to stress is age-old: it evolved so that people could cope with predators, hunger and extremes of temperature, etc. These were things prehistoric people encountered regularly in their lives. However, such stress reactions are often not appropriate in modern society, and stress can now induce illness in people instead. Stress causes the body to secrete the hormone adrenaline. The effects of adrenaline are shown in Figure 2.23. Anyone who is stressed every day for a period of time is likely to develop heart and breathing problems.

Personal hygiene

Good personal hygiene is essential to us all: our skin, hair, and teeth soon start to lose their sparkle if not maintained properly (see Figure 2.24). When working in the field of health and social care, you will have to work closely with other people. Poor personal hygiene is very noticeable if in a combined space and can cause embarrassment and discomfort for everyone.

Poor personal hygiene isn't just unpleasant, it can affect our health in a negative way. Human beings are an ideal medium for bacteria to grow in. We are the right sort of temperature, we produce moisture in the form of sweat, and we produce food for bacteria in the form of dead skin cells, and in the chemicals in our sweat. Bacteria can be passed from one person to another and also on to food, so it's important to try to reduce the number of bacteria that are using us as host.

Watch the people in the room with you. See how often they touch their faces, scratch itches, play

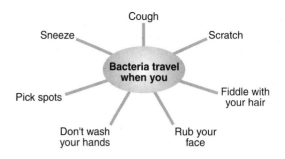

Figure 2.25   How we pass on bacteria

with their hair and rub their noses. Every time they do this they are transferring bacteria from one place to another (see Figure 2.25). Not only are they increasing the risk of spreading bacteria to themselves, they are also increasing the chances of spreading bacteria to others.

Examples of infections that can be passed on as a result of poor hygiene are headlice, threadworms, ringworm, impetigo and scabies.

Lack of physical exercise

A lack of physical exercise has many effects on our bodies (see Figure 2.26). Our lungs are never fully inflated and deposits collect at their bases. The bowel is sluggish and this leads to constipation. Our weight is not under control and, frequently, as middle age sets in, our body weight increases steadily.

Figure 2.24   Good personal hygiene is essential

Figure 2.26   The effects of lack of exercise

Sexual behaviour

The continuation of the human race depends upon males and females having sex, and sex is therefore a natural part of human life. Because people are actively engaging in sex at younger and younger ages, they are often not aware of the consequences of unwanted pregnancies, and of the possibilities of contracting diseases that are transmitted through the act of sexual intercourse.

Sex is exciting and pleasurable to both partners, and is a way of demonstrating love and affection for each other. Sex can occur between males and females or between two people of the same gender. The latter cannot result in pregnancy, but still carries a serious risk of disease. It doesn't matter whether the relationship is for one night or many nights, the risk of disease is still there. However, the greater the number of sexual partners a person has, the greater the risk of being infected with disease and the greater the risk of passing it on.

HIV (human inmmunodeficiency virus) and AIDS (acquired immune deficiency syndrome)

AIDS is caused by the HIV virus and, although only first reported as recently as 1981, AIDS is now a major worldwide epidemic. AIDS is the term used to describe the condition people who have advanced HIV infection suffer from. There is no cure for AIDS (although several therapies are now known to prolong the life expectancy of AIDS sufferers and some vaccines are now being tested on people). Therefore the only way to avoid HIV infection is to avoid behaviours that put a person at risk of contracting the virus. This means we should not have unprotected sex and drug users should not share needles.

HIV damages the human immune system by killing or injuring the immune cells such that the person's body is unable to fight off certain infections and cancers (see Figure 2.27). Generally, the AIDS victim is prone to **opportunistic infections** and cancers that do not usually cause illness in healthy people.

HIV/AIDS statistics

You will find the latest statistics on the Internet (www.avert.org/wwstatsy.htm). Statistics for the UK are given in Figure 2.28.

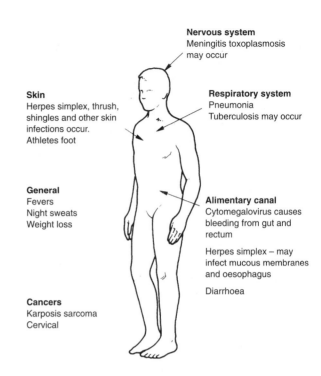

Skin
Herpes simplex, thrush, shingles and other skin infections occur.
Athletes foot

General
Fevers
Night sweats
Weight loss

Cancers
Karposis sarcoma
Cervical

Nervous system
Meningitis toxoplasmosis may occur

Respiratory system
Pneumonia
Tuberculosis may occur

Alimentary canal
Cytomegalovirus causes bleeding from gut and rectum

Herpes simplex – may infect mucous membranes and oesophagus

Diarrhoea

Figure 2.27   AIDS-related illnesses

The figures in Figure 2.28 show only reported cases. As many people are unaware they are infected with the HIV virus, real figures will be much higher (it can take several months for HIV antibodies to develop and show up in tests). Clients and care-workers who have HIV infection, and those people who work with clients who have HIV infection, require information, tact, full treatment and support.

Examine Figure 2.28.

1   Calculate the percentage increase or decrease in cases of HIV and AIDS in each country between the years 1995 and 1998.

2   Comment on each country's apparent success in the promotion of health in relation to HIV and AIDS as suggested by these figures.

Examples of a calculation

Percentage increase of HIV cases between 1990 and 1991 in England = 2250 – 1969 × 100 = 37.8% increase in cases of HIV.

Figure 2.28 Table to show HIV and AIDS statistics in the different countries of the United Kingdom by year by kind permission of the Public Health Laboratory Service AIDS Centre

Year	Country							
	England		Wales		Scotland		N. Ireland	
	HIV-infected persons	AIDS cases	HIV-infected persons	AIDS cases	HIV-infected persons	AIDS cases	HIV-infected persons	AIDS cases
All to 1984	87	100	0	3	213	3	0	0
1985	2224	151	13	2	249	4	20	1
1986	2226	285	27	4	334	7	12	1
1987	2024	602	27	9	259	25	8	2
1988	1429	699	44	16	140	34	8	5
1989	1531	766	29	14	130	57	12	5
1990	1969	1177	67	16	130	62	12	8
1991	2250	1246	31	14	159	86	15	4
1992	2192	1370	46	17	135	77	16	7
1993	2153	1457	38	21	147	111	11	9
1994	2168	1622	45	23	137	121	7	7
1995	2432	1409	43	20	158	130	15	13
1996	2606	1738	38	12	159	94	10	10
1997	2331	1275	32	35	170	68	14	0
1998	2599	882	37	22	160	56	11	4
1999*	1320	368	27	10	71	33	4	1
Total	31541	15147	544	238	2751	968	175	77

* Only half-year figures for 1999 are available

> **Think it over**
> Look again at the trends and patterns of HIV and AIDS in the UK. Compile graphs or pie charts from the data provided. You could also write a short report that identifies the main trends of HIV and AIDS infection.

Transmission

Main ways in which the virus is passed on to others are as follows (see Figure 2.29):

- Unprotected sexual contact with an infected partner.

- The sharing of blood-contaminated needles or syringes between injecting drug users when one or more of the individuals is infected with the virus.

- An infected mother can pass the infection on to her baby during pregnancy or at birth.

Although rare, HIV can also arise from:

- Contact with infected blood. Blood donations are now screened and treated to destroy the virus (but this was not the case before 1985).

- Accidental jabs or cuts with needles, sharps and medical instruments when passed between an infected client and health care worker (and vice versa).

To date, scientists have found no evidence of transmission through:

- saliva, sweat, tears, urine or faeces

- towels, bedding, toilet seats, swimming pools, telephones or food utensils

- mosquitoes, bed bugs, or other biting insects.

Figure 2.29 Analysis of routes of HIV and AIDS infection for the United Kingdom for all cases between 1984 and 1998

Routes for infection	AIDS cases	HIV cases
Sex between men (homosexual route)	10771	23226
Sex between men and women (heterosexual route)	2715	8568
Injecting drug users	1030	3489
Exchanging blood or tissue	764	1622
Unknown	457	1672

Try it out

Look at Figure 2.29. Find the percentage of HIV-imfected persons who were injecting drug users. Calculate the percentage of people with AIDS infected by the heterosexual route.

Note: Having other sexually transmitted diseases, such as herpes, syphilis and gonorrhoea, seems to make sufferers more susceptible to HIV infection if they have intercourse with an HIV-infected person.

To protect yourself from HIV infection you should:

1   Practise safe sex (using kite marked condoms) or celibacy.

2   Limit the number of partners you have or wait until you are in a permanent relationship before having sex.

3   Wipe surfaces with good disinfectant after cleaning up spills of any body fluids.

4   Wear disposable gloves when dealing with blood, body fluids or wounds.

?

The number of people who become infected by the heterosexual route each year is rapidly overtaking the number of people infected by the homosexual route. HIV infection can no longer be considered a disease of 'gays'. Overall figures for HIV infection suggest a further increase in 1999. The health promotion message for safe sex – use a condom – is not getting through to a large number of the population.

Unsafe practices in the workplace

Workplaces are subject to various inspection systems and must comply with the Health and Safety at Work Act 1974 and the 1988 Control of Substances Hazardous to Health Regulations. The key features of the Health and Safety at Work Act (HASAW) are given in Figure 2.30. What HASAW basically means is that both the employer and the

- *employers must make all reasonable efforts to ensure the health, safety and welfare of all their employees by informing you:*

–how to carry out your job safely without risk to yourself and others

–of risks identified with the job that may affect you

–what measures have been taken to protect you from the identified risks

–and how to use these measures

–how to get first aid treatment

–what to do in an emergency

–by leaflet or poster about the Health and Safety at Work Act and the local Health and Safety Executive's address

- *employers must provide free of charge:*

–adequate safety training

–clothing or equipment required to protect you while at work

- *as an employee, your responsibilities are:*

–to take reasonable care of yourself and others (including the general public) who may be affected by your work

–use any equipment provided for you for its intended purpose and in a proper manner

–not to carry out tasks that you do not know how to do safely

–let your manager know if you witness anything that is not safe and could place yourself or others at risk

–to co-operate with employers on health and safety matters

–inform the appropriate person in the organisation if you have an accident or witness a near miss

Figure 2.30   Key features of the Health and Safety at Work Act 1974

Figure 2.31 How the Health and Safety at Work Act affects care settings

employee share extra responsibilities for health and safety and that any organisation employing more than five people must have a written policy statement on health and safety. Figure 2.31 outlines the ways HASAW affects care settings.

The main requirements of the Control of Substances Hazardous to Health (COSHH) Regulations are that employers must:

⬦ complete risk assessments on all hazardous substances used in the workplace

⬦ keep records of risk assessments and review them regularly

⬦ inform employees about any substance hazardous to their health

⬦ provide appropriate training in the use of hazardous substances.

Hazardous substances include correction fluid used in offices, disinfectants used for cleaning, drugs used in medical treatment and radioactive chemicals used in care settings.

Workplaces contain people, and people often take shortcuts to save themselves time or consider certain things they must do in the course of the jobs irrelevant or a waste of time. As a result, people often don't wear their protective clothing properly, they don't wear ear protectors against noise and fail to wear safety helmets and shoes and other safety clothing. Circuit breakers (designed to protect equipment) could be jammed open, the wrong fuses might be installed in plugs, incorrect waste disposal methods might be practised – a host of unsafe working methods could be mentioned. We must all be aware of hazards and unsafe practices in the workplace. We must investigate these and, if necessary, report them. Remember the responsibility for health and safety rests with all of us.

Health promotion

One way to promote people's health is to produce leaflets and brochures (Figure 2.32). Your tutor may have collected samples of these for you to study. Other good sources of such literature include:

⬦ doctors' surgeries

⬦ dentists' surgeries

⬦ health centres

⬦ health visitors

⬦ health promotion units

⬦ supermarkets

⬦ health food shops

⬦ specialist support agencies.

Figure 2.32 Some examples of health promotion literature

When collecting leaflets for use in your assignments, think carefully about what kind of information you need and who you intend to read it. For example, a child will not want to be told about kilojoule values or the risks of eating too much saturated fat. Similarly, a well-educated adult will not appreciate leaflets that contain lots of smiley faces faces eating high-fibre bread and fresh vegetables. You should also avoid those leaflets food manufacturers publish simply to promote their own products.

Not everything we read is 100% accurate. You will have to study the information carefully to assess whether it reflects the particular points you wish to make (see Figure 2.33). If you do not care for published material, you could make leaflets or posters of your own.

Figure 2.33   Assessing health promotion literature

Indicators of physical good health

There are a number of different physical (body) measurements that can be taken to assess a person's state of health. These include:

◦   height and weight

◦   peak flow

◦   body mass index (BMI)

◦   resting pulse rate and recovery after exercise.

Height and weight

There are standard ways of measuring a person's weight against that person's height. To do this, standard charts or tables are used that are available in three different forms. These different forms take into account the person's frame size. Frame size is a person's bone size and build. If you find it difficult to judge a person's frame size, ask him or her: most people know whether standard clothing and shoe sizes fit them and will be able to guide you as to their frame. Different tables are also used for men and women (see Figures 2.35 and 2.36).

If someone falls into the severely overweight range, he or she is at risk of cardiovascular disease, high blood pressure, diabetes, arthritis and other conditions. Such people should be advised to seek help from their family doctor.

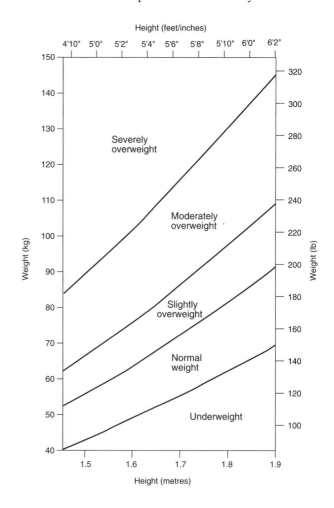

Figure 2.34   Example of a height/weight chart

Men													
Height (in shoes)		Weight											
		Small frame					Medium frame					Large frame	
m	ft in	kg kg	st lb	–	st lb		kg kg	st lb	–	st lb	kg kg	st lb	– st lb
1.575	5 2	50.8–54.4	8 0	–	8 8		53.5–58.5	8 6	–	9 3	57.2–64.0	9 0	– 10 1
1.6	5 3	52.2–55.8	8 3	–	8 11		54.9–60.3	8 9	–	9 7	58.5–65.3	9 3	– 10 4
1.626	5 4	53.5–57.2	8 6	–	9 0		56.2–64.7	8 12	–	9 10	59.9–67.1	9 6	– 10 8
1.651	5 5	54.9–58.5	8 9	–	9 3		57.6–63.0	9 1	–	9 13	61.2–68.9	9 9	– 10 12
1.676	5 6	56.2–60.3	9 12	–	9 7		59.0–64.9	9 4	–	10 3	62.6–70.8	10 12	– 11 2
1.702	5 7	58.1–62.1	9 2	–	9 11		60.8–66.7	9 8	–	10 7	64.4–73.0	10 2	– 11 7
1.727	5 8	59.9–64.0	9 6	–	10 1		62.6–68.9	9 12	–	10 12	66.7–75.3	10 7	– 11 12
1.753	5 9	61.7–65.8	9 10	–	10 5		64.4–70.8	10 2	–	11 2	68.5–77.1	10 11	– 12 2
1.778	5 10	63.5–68.0	10 0	–	10 10		66.2–72.6	10 6	–	11 6	70.3–78.9	11 1	– 12 6
1.803	5 11	65.2–69.9	10 4	–	11 0		68.0–74.8	10 10	–	11 11	72.1–81.2	11 5	– 12 11
1.829	6 0	67.1–71.7	10 8	–	11 4		69.9–77.1	11 0	–	12 2	74.4–83.5	11 10	– 13 2
1.854	6 1	68.9–73.5	10 12	–	11 8		71.7–79.4	11 4	–	12 7	76.2–85.7	12 0	– 13 7
1.88	6 2	70.8–75.7	11 0	–	11 13		73.5–81.6	11 8	–	12 12	78.5–88.0	12 5	– 13 12
1.905	6 3	72.6–77.6	11 4	–	12 3		75.7–83.5	11 13	–	13 3	80.7–90.3	12 10	– 14 3
1.93	6 4	74.4–79.4	11 8	–	12 7		78.1–86.2	12 4	–	13 8	82.7–92.5	13 0	– 14 8

Figure 2.35 Weight/height chart for men

Women													
Height (in shoes)		Weight											
		Small frame					Medium frame					Large frame	
m	ft in	kg kg	st lb	–	st lb		kg kg	st lb	–	st lb	kg kg	st lb	– st lb
1.473	4 10	41.7–44.5	6 8	–	7 0		43.5–48.5	6 12	–	7 9	47.2–54.0	7 6	– 8 7
1.499	4 11	42.6–45.8	6 10	–	7 3		44.5–49.9	7 0	–	7 12	48.1–55.3	7 8	– 8 10
1.524	5 0	43.5–47.2	6 12	–	7 6		45.8–51.3	7 3	–	8 1	49.4–56.7	7 11	– 8 13
1.549	5 1	44.9–48.5	7 1	–	7 9		47.2–52.6	7 6	–	8 4	50.8–58.1	8 0	– 9 2
1.575	5 2	46.3–49.9	7 4	–	7 12		48.5–54.0	7 9	–	8 7	52.2–59.4	8 3	– 9 5
1.6	5 3	47.6–51.3	7 7	–	8 1		49.9–55.3	7 12	–	8 10	53.5–60.8	8 6	– 9 8
1.626	5 4	49.0–52.6	7 10	–	8 4		51.3–57.2	8 1	–	9 0	54.9–62.6	8 10	– 9 12
1.651	5 5	50.3–54.0	7 13	–	8 7		52.7–59.0	8 4	–	9 4	56.8–64.4	8 13	– 10 2
1.676	5 6	51.7–55.8	8 2	–	8 11		54.4–61.2	8 8	–	9 9	58.5–66.2	9 3	– 10 6
1.702	5 7	53.5–57.6	8 6	–	9 1		56.2–63.0	8 12	–	9 13	60.3–68.0	9 7	– 10 10
1.727	5 8	55.3–59.4	8 10	–	9 5		58.1–64.9	9 2	–	10 3	62.1–69.9	9 11	– 11 0
1.753	5 9	57.2–61.2	9 0	–	9 9		59.9–66.7	9 6	–	10 7	64.0–71.7	10 1	– 11 4
1.778	5 10	59.0–63.5	9 4	–	10 0		61.7–68.5	9 10	–	10 11	65.8–73.9	10 5	– 11 9
1.803	5 11	60.8–65.3	9 8	–	10 4		63.5–70.3	10 0	–	11 1	67.6–76.2	10 9	– 12 0
1.829	6 0	62.6–67.1	9 12	–	10 8		65.3–72.1	10 4	–	11 5	69.4–78.5	10 13	– 12 5

Figure 2.36 Weight/height chart for women

Moderately overweight people are still at risk and should follow the same plan as severely overweight people. Slightly overweight people are still at greater risk than those of normal weight, but should follow a sensible weight-reducing plan and take more exercise. Anyone with health problems should be advised to consult his or her family doctor before beginning a new regime.

Being slightly underweight is not a problem but being very underweight *is* a problem. If someone has recently started to lose weight for no reason he or she may have an undiagnosed illness. Such people should be advised to consult a medical practitioner.

Some people (and not just overweight people) are very sensitive about other knowing their weight. When working with people you will have to anticipate such sensitivity. People might be able to weigh themselves and be able to find their position on the weight/height charts themselves. Do not tell other people about someone's weight without first asking the person for his or her permission to do so. If you are taking measurements from children, ask for the child's permission as well as asking his or her parents or guardians.

Peak flow

To measure peak flow you need a meter which records the maximum speed at which air can flow out of the lungs. This measurement is used to assess the width of the air passages (bronchi). The most common use of peak flow measurement is to monitor the degree of bronchospasm (narrowing of the air passages) in people who suffer from asthma, and their response to the drugs they take for the condition. It is also a useful measurement in people who have respiratory problems, such as intermittent coughing or difficulty with breathing. It can help to asses whether they have developed asthma (see Figure 2.37).

Figure 2.37   A peak flow meter

After first taking a deep breath, an individual blows through the mouthpiece with maximum effort. Fitness suites in gyms and sports centres often employ peak flow measuring equipment.

Body mass index

The body mass index (BMI) also uses weight in kilograms and height in metres to assess people's general state of health. BMI is worked out using the following calculation:

$$\frac{\text{weight (kg)}}{\text{height (m)}^2} = \text{BMI}$$

For example, if your height is 1.82 m, then you will divide your weight by 1.82 x 1.82. If your weight is 70.5 kg then:

$$\frac{70.5}{1.82 \times 1.82} = 21.3$$

People with BMIs between 19 and 22 appear to live the longest; death rates appear to be the highest in people with BMIs of 25 and over. BMIs are different for males and females (see Figure 2.38).

Figure 2.38 Body mass indexes

Female	Significance	Male	Significance
Less than 18	Underweight	Less than 18	Underweight
18–20	Lean	18–20	Lean
21–22	Average	21–23	Average
23–28	Plump	24–32	Plump
29–36	Moderately obese	32–40	Moderately obese
37+	Severely obese	40+	Severely obese

Try it out

You will find lots of useful references to BMIs and other physical measurements if you 'surf the web'. Some Internet health sites can be found in the 'Further reading' section at the end of the book.

Resting pulse rate and recovery after exercise

You can count someone's pulse rate where an artery crosses a bone. Pulse rates are usually taken either below the base of the thumb or on one side of the windpipe in the neck. It should be counted by lightly pressing two figures over the site until you feel the throbbing. Count the beats over 10 or 15 second intervals and multiply by 6 or 4, accordingly, to obtain the number of beats over one minute.

To take people's resting pulse, make sure they are calm and have been sitting quietly for 5–10 minutes. Take at least three recordings and calculate the average pulse rate. (To work out the average, add all the readings together and divide by the number you obtain by the number of readings you have taken).

Zola had the following counts for her resting pulse rate:

65 68 72 74 68 65

The average would be 65 + 68 + 72 + 74 + 68 + 65 divided by 6. This works out at 69 beats per minute.

Working in pairs, take physical measurements of members of your group. Record your results in a table.

Discuss what the results suggest about each individual's level of fitness.

It is generally accepted that the lower the pulse rate in a healthy individual, the fitter he or she is. After exercise, when the pulse rate has increased, the same principle still applies.

To measure someone's 'recovery after exercise' pulse rate, you will need to provide your subject with some form of mild exercise, such as running on the spot or walking up and down stairs. Take readings immediately after the exercise and every minute until the pulse rate is back to resting level. You could draw up a graph of pulse rate against time to display your readings, and mark the point at which the resting pulse rate is regained. Note the time it took for this to occur.

To obtain valid results repeat this over three or four exercises and work out the average.

Safety note: When devising the exercise, bear in mind your subject's state of health and fitness! You could not ask an elderly lady to jog around the block! Walking up a flight of stairs might similarly be too much, so stepping up and down one step a few times might be sufficient.

The shorter the recovery time, the fitter the individual. Pulse rates should generally recover within 2 or 3 minutes but, again, bear in mind the severity of the exercise you have asked someone to do.

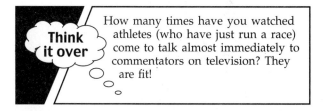

Think it over

How many times have you watched athletes (who have just run a race) come to talk almost immediately to commentators on television? They are fit!

To find out about negotiating health improvement plans with clients, see the assessment activities section, which follows.

Unit 2 Assessment

Obtaining a Pass grade

To obtain a *Pass*, you need to produce a plan to promote the health and well-being of at least one person whose health is at risk. This plan must include:

- information about the health risks
- an explanation of which risks the person can control
- at least two measures of health
- timescales and targets for improving the person's health

supplementary health promotion material.

1   Study the outline profiles of the pretend family members shown in Figure 2.39 below. All these people have health risks. If you had to construct a health plan for one of these people, which one would you choose? At first sight June's may seem the easiest to work out, Julie's perhaps the hardest.

June may appear to be a good choice, but a successful plan would depend on her desire for change. Jason may think a health plan is a big joke and may not take it seriously.

June – 71 years old, low income (state pension), fries most meals, eats little protein; she had a small stroke 2 years ago; she smokes, takes no exercise, rarely goes out; she lives in a cold flat, watches TV too much. Only sees family, has no friends

Julie, 42 years old, single parent, has two part-time jobs; works hard to make ends meet; worries about her children; had lump in breast removed last year

Health plan

Jill, 18-years old, engaged to Jason, may have unprotected sex, eats mostly burgers and chips for main meals

18-year-old Jason rides a motorbike, drinks a lot of alcohol, smokes, takes ecstasy occasionally, has unsafe sex; well paid assembly line work; listens to loud music through ear phones

Figure 2.39   Possible subjects for a health plan

It is hence important to give serious thought to whom you choose for your health plan, and the reasons why, before starting to collect your assignment evidence. Try not to choose the easiest person you can think of as this might limit your opportunities. In real life, the best advice is to talk to the person first about what you need to do to get his or her support for a health improvement plan. You *must* be tactful: think how you would feel if one of your friends or family decided you were 'unhealthy' and tried to change your lifestyle! It might be best to explain your task to more than one person to see what their reactions are before making your final decision. Having made your choice, discuss this with your tutor. He or she will be able to guide you.

2   Having identified the person you will provide the health plan for, you must now give some thought to the format in which you will present the plan. The most obvious way to present it is probably in table form. However, is your person a good reader and will he or she be able to understand tables? A child, an older person or an adult with learning disabilities will prefer larger, clear typing and lots of illustrations. A friend who is a student at college or university may be used to reading tables, but a person with a visual impairment might appreciate an audiotape. Many educational establishments also have the facilities for converting written notes into Braille.

3   You could produce a booklet or a large poster that could be put on display on the person's kitchen wall. Whatever form your plan takes, you must have valid reasons for the design you have chosen, and it must be easily understood by your subject.

You are required to consider both short and long-term targets for improving a person's health. Wherever possible, these targets should be measurable.

Try it out

Study the family members shown in Figure 2.39 once more.

How could members of the family control some of the health risks they face?

How could you measure their weight and overall fitness? How would you go about assessing their diets?

Obtaining a Merit grade:

1   Read the case study about Vikram. To obtain a *Merit*, you will have to relate the physical measurements you have taken from Vikram to his personal circumstances (i.e. explain how the results you have obtained in the height/weight tables, in measurements of his resting and recovery pulse rates and of his BMI, relate to Vikram's current diet and level of exercise).

2   You will also need to explain the links between his physical health and his emotional, social and intellectual health. For example, his inability to find a job may relate to his emotional stress and to the low feelings he has about himself.

3   You also need to explain why you have chosen the specific health promotion materials you have provided (e.g. lots of attractive illustrations, non-technical language, targeting people in Vikram's age range, not tied to commercial interests – particularly the healthy eating literature).

4   When you have constructed your plan, you will have to talk it through with your subject. Although you will have given a great deal of thought to your plan and will have chosen your subject carefully, when it comes to implementing it you may well find your subject is not so keen! No one likes to be dictated to, and people often dig their heels in and refuse to listen to advice.

CASE STUDY – Vikram

Vikram is 16 years old, is moderately overweight, smokes but doesn't drink alcohol, takes no exercise, and suffers from moderate stress due to a lack of money and because of criticism at home as he is unemployed. He has no important qualifications from school, but he has some Amateur Swimming Association certificates, including a 400-metre award.

The possible health targets you could produce for Vikram are outlined below:

Overweight   Provide a sensible eating plan and expect (with the exercise plan) Vikram to lose 7 kg in four to six weeks (short term) and 15 kg in the next 12 months (long term).

Smoking   Reduce from 40 cigarettes a day to 20 cigarettes in one month and none in 12 months.

Exercise   The chosen exercise (negotiated with Vikram) is swimming – 10 lengths of the baths, three times per week for one month stepped up to 25 lengths, three times per week in six months. In one year's time, to have improved his swimming techniques and to have joined a water polo training club. Swimming to be funded by savings on cigarettes consumed. Consider lifesaving training when his swimming skills are improved.

Stress   Provide social and physical targets that will help him alleviate his stress. Vikram will have a focus for his daily activities. While he still has time for job-searching, he might also have, in due course, a job possibility as a pool attendant if he manages to succeed on the lifesaving course. His self-esteem should rise and he

should become more confident as his skills improve.

You would need to explain these targets clearly to Vikram, and provide him with some health promotional literature to support your plan. These would need to be in a language he will understand and not too technical.

You might visit your local health education unit to find leaflets on:

- reducing smoking
- healthy eating
- the benefits of exercise
- coping with stress.

In addition, Vikram would probably find it helpful if you supplied him with information appropriate to his exercise targets (swimming pool costs, opening times, etc.) and about the skills required to join a water polo team.

Vikram

5   When people understand the reasons for doing or not doing things they are more likely to listen – so explain your reasons carefully. Do not expect people to change their habits or lifestyle overnight: be prepared to change your timings and

be open to compromise. If someone smokes 40 cigarettes a day, you will get a better response if you gradually lower his or her habit to 30, then 20, 10 and finally single figures than if you suggest he or she stops smoking immediately. And you must also give him or her plenty of encouragement.

6   Discussing the health improvements you wish to achieve with your subject will make your plan much more effective. Give the person time to think about what you have said, and bring the issues up at appropriate, quieter moments. Don't 'nag' or get irritated or become

---

Try it out

Study the following people who might have been chosen to follow a health plan:

1   A busy, working mother who has a job that means sitting at a desk all day. Your plan suggests she exercises twice a week. However, your subject complains that she never has time for exercise and doesn't like it anyway.

2   Your friend's good-looking brother is very proud of his large number of 'girlfriends' – mostly single-night relationships. He does not practise safe sex and considers himself to be immune to sexually transmitted diseases.

3   Your subject is a 55-year-old relative who lives alone and exists mainly on fried foods (because he or she is not a good cook, and frying is quick and easy).

In pairs, take it in turns to role play, first, the subject and, secondly, the person who has devised the plan. When role playing the person who has devised the plan, be particularly careful to *negotiate*. Remember, people are much more likely to accept your plans if they feel they have been involved in devising them and if they feel they have been consulted first.

---

discouraged. Quiet encouragement and praise are far more likely to be effective.

Obtaining a Distinction grade

1   You will need to predict the physical, social and emotional effects on Vikram if he followed your plan. Discussing these effects with him might be a prime motivator for Vikram following your plan. You will need to be aware of Vikram's responses when he seems to have reached a limit or plateau, or even if he fails. Will this leave him with less self-esteem than before? When he 'plateaus' out, you might be able to suggest some workouts in a fitness suite so that he can develop more physical strength.

2   You will also need to anticipate difficulties and suggest ways to overcome them. For instance, Vikram will not be able to afford the swimming sessions if he cannot reduce his tobacco consumption. You might question him about his smoking habits and suggest ways to avoid temptation. If he smokes more when he is at home because other people at home smoke, then he should get away from home for longer periods. If he smokes with his friends, then perhaps he can suggest ways to involve his friends in more active pursuits, such as badminton, football or basketball.

3   If Vikram eats out at snack and coffee bars, he will have difficulty keeping to a healthy eating diet, but he might improve relationships at home by volunteering to prepare some meals – which will help to improve his diet at the same time. This will also save money.

4   To obtain a distinction, your plan must be detailed and it must address all relevant areas using the appropriate technical language.

Unit 2 Test

1   Which of the following diseases have been identified as risks associated with smoking?

   a Heart disease.
   b Diabetes.
   c Arthritis.
   d Tuberculosis.

2   Stress can produce:

   a lowered immunity to disease
   b heart disease
   c anaemia
   d vitamin deficiency.

3   Which of the following is an example of unsafe practices in the workplace?

   a Unhealthy diet.
   b Being overweight.
   c Not wearing ear protectors.
   d Not taking exercise.

4   Which of these is known as the body mass index?

   a Height divided by weight.
   b Height divided by weight squared.
   c Weight divided by height.
   d Weight divided by height squared.

5   A peak flow meter is used to measure:

   a maximum speed of heart rate
   b maximum speed of expired air
   c maximum speed of inhaled air
   d breathing rate.

6   Janis has difficulty forming relationships with colleagues. This is an aspect of his:

   a physical health
   b emotional health
   c social health
   d intellectual health.

7   The normal recovery rate of the pulse to its resting state is in the range of:

   a 6–8 minutes
   b 6–8 seconds

   c 2–4 seconds
   d 2–4 minutes.

8   Which of the following diseases are associated with being overweight?

   a Tuberculosis.
   b Heart disease.
   c Lung cancer.
   d Arthritis.

9   Professional people, such as doctors and lawyers, are in social class:

   a I
   b V
   c IV
   d II.

10   Which of the following deficiencies is most likely to give rise to anaemia?

   a Lack of calcium.
   b Lack of Vitamin D.
   c Lack of iron.
   d Lack of protein.

11   Modern definitions of health focus on:

   a experts defining health
   b complete physical and emotional well-being
   c absence of illness and infirmity
   d people's aspirations and their quality of life.

12   Define a balanced diet.

13   Provide three recommendations for people who want to follow a healthy diet.

14   Explain the benefits of a diet that contains the recommended amount of fibre.

15   Describe the uses of protein, fat and carbohydrate within the human body.

16   Explain why older people require fewer energy-containing foods than adolescents.

17 Write a few paragraphs about health needs and relate these to one social class.

18 Explain why fresh fruit and vegetables are recommended in balanced diets.

19 Describe four sources of health promotion literature.

20 List four potential difficulties people might encounter in keeping to a health plan.

UNIT 2 ASSESSMENT

Understanding personal development

This Unit covers the knowledge you will need in order to meet the assessment requirements for Unit 3. It is written in five sections.

Section one looks at human growth and development and the five main stages of human life. Section two considers how social and economic factors affect human development. Section three explores the idea of self-concept and analyses those factors that influence the self-concepts we hold about ourselves. Section four looks at the changes we all experience during the course of our lives. Finally, section five considers the support carers can give people when they have to cope with change in their lives.

Further information and advice for meeting the assessment requirements for the Unit (in particular, for Merit and Distinction level work) are at the end of the Unit.

Also at the end of the Unit is a test to check your understanding: this includes two scenarios for you to analyse and discuss.

Human growth and development

Life is about change: each year we live we notice changes in our body. As we live our lives we learn new skills and knowledge – we develop intellectually. As we develop we experience changes in the way we feel about ourselves and others; our emotions develop and change. Throughout life we find ourselves in different social situations and relationships – we develop socially.

One way of looking at the human life-span is to study the way we develop physically, intellectually, emotionally and socially. The first letters of these words spell **PIES**. Unit 2 explains that PIES is a way of thinking about human development.

This section explores physical, intellectual, emotional and social development at five **life stages**: infancy, early childhood, puberty/adolescence, adulthood and old age.

At one time life was considered to be a simple set of stages. During infancy, childhood and adolescence, a person would grow physically and learn the knowledge and skills he or she needed for work. Adulthood was a time when people worked and/or brought up their own family. Old age was when people retired and children would usually be grown up by the time their parents reached retirement.

At the beginning of the twenty-first century people's lives are much more complex. People now need constantly to relearn skills and to increase their knowledge because they are often required to change the kind of work they do. Some people have children late in life; some choose not to have children. Science now makes it possible for a woman to give birth in her 50s. Some people may 'retire' in their 30s or 40s – perhaps for a while before taking up employment again! Life stages are no longer as clear as they once were, and some writers now prefer to see life as a continuous process of change rather than a series of distinct stages. However, this section explores the five stages people still commonly use to categorise human development.

Infancy

Physical development

Growth is defined biologically by three stages:

* increase in the number of body cells

* increase in the size of individual cells as they carry more material

* body cells becoming more specialised in both structure and function.

All three stages are very important in a foetus's growth and development. However, after birth, it is the increases in the number of body cells and in the size of cells that are the most important factors in the infant's development.

At birth, on average, babies have a 'length' (later called 'height') of 50 cm and a weight of 3.5 kg. For a few days, babies lose weight as they learn to feed, but rapidly regain their birth weight. A baby's head circumference is also measured at birth and for a short while afterwards. This measurement is used to assess brain growth.

New-born babies are often known as **neonates**. Although they are helpless and would die if they were not cared for, human neonates show a surprising number of inborn physical reflexes. A reflex is an automatic response. Most of these fade away as babies become more mature, and other reflexes take their place.

Neonate reflexes

* *Suckling reflex*: Babies automatically suck on anything placed in their mouths.

* *Rooting reflex*: babies turn their heads when their faces are touched. They are trying to find their mother's nipple.

* *Stepping or walking reflex*: when the babies are supported and their feet are allowed to touch a solid surface, their legs move in an action resembling stepping or walking.

* *Startle reflex*: if babies are surprised by a loud noise, they pull up their arms and legs and ball their fists. (This is very similar to the Moro reflex, but in the Moro reflex the arms are extended and the hands are open.)

* *Plantar reflex*: when the sole of a baby's foot is stroked, the big toe curls upwards. (Plantar means referring to the sole of the foot.)

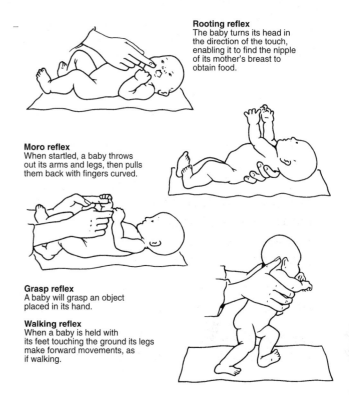

Rooting reflex
The baby turns its head in the direction of the touch, enabling it to find the nipple of its mother's breast to obtain food.

Moro reflex
When startled, a baby throws out its arms and legs, then pulls them back with fingers curved.

Grasp reflex
A baby will grasp an object placed in its hand.

Walking reflex
When a baby is held with its feet touching the ground its legs make forward movements, as if walking.

Figure 3.1 The primitive reflexes of a new-born baby

* *Grasping reflex*: babies hold on tightly to any objects placed in their hands.

In addition to these primitive reflexes, new-born babies will be able to recognise different colours and tastes, and be able to smell, and to hear and to blink their eyes. Babies have to learn to control their bodies. Learning to control the use of large muscles is called learning to use our gross **motor skills**.

Gross motor skills
Head control

Until they reach the age of about 4 months, when babies are pulled to sit from a lying position, their heads will fall back. Gradually they increase their control of their heads and, during the fifth and sixth months, they will have learnt to lift their heads when being pulled to a sitting position. When held in a sitting position, their heads fall forward until they are 1 month old, when babies begin to lift their heads for a few seconds. After a further four weeks, they can hold their heads up.

Sitting

At 4 months of age, when held while sitting, a baby's back is nearly straight. By 6 months, infants can sit by themselves with support from their arms held out in front of them. Two months later, infants can sit easily with no support and, close to their first birthday, they can turn sideways while sitting without toppling over.

Crawling and walking

At around 11 or 12 months of age, many babies can walk holding onto an adult's hands

Around the age of 2 months, babies lie flat when placed face down on the floor with their legs extended behind. They can lift their heads off the floor for a few seconds at a time but, a month later, they can hold the weight of their upper bodies on their forearms and lift their heads for much longer periods. At the same time, if babies are held upright, they cannot support themselves at all whereas, at 6 months, they can bear their full weight when held.

At 10 months, most babies will be able to crawl using their hands and knees and be able to stand without being held, but by holding on to furniture. Just before their first birthday, many can walk holding an adult's two hands, gradually needing only one. A big occasion is when a baby takes his or her first steps alone. This is usually around 13–15 months of age. Some babies 'bear-walk' in-between crawling and walking – this is moving on all fours using both hands and feet. Others never crawl, but move around on their bottoms in a sitting position, so-called 'shuffling', using their arms to push them around.

Fine motor skills from birth to 1 year.

Fine motor skills mean learning to use small muscles to control an action. This is more difficult for babies to do than gross motor actions.

Almost from birth, babies will look at bright lights and shiny objects. By the second month, they will gaze intently at the carer's face and begin to reach out to get hold of a finger. By 3 months, babies turn their heads to follow an adult, can hold a rattle for a few moments and play with their own hands.

By 9 months, objects can be transferred from hand to hand and the pincer grip between thumb and forefinger is developing to pick up small objects. Babies now look for fallen objects and explore everything they can by putting things in their mouths – the most sensitive area for touch.

At the end of the first year, babies throw things deliberately, can eat with their fingers and can manage a spoon, if allowed. The pincer movement is well developed, enabling even small things to be picked up, and babies love to point to and to copy the actions of other people.

 **Think it over** Either by yourself or in pairs, think of babies you know well and discuss the developments you have noticed in the last few months.

At the end of the first year, how have the standard height and weight measurements changed? (If you need to refresh your memory about these charts, look back to Unit 2.)

Babies now weigh three times their birth weight and have grown half as much again as their birth length. Their limbs have increased in size so that their heads are smaller in proportion to the rest of their bodies, but their heads have not shrunk (Figure 3.3)!

Both gross and fine motor skills develop rapidly between 1 year and 18 months.

With increasing confidence in walking, and a growing ability to carry things around and climb steps, infants are likely to fall down a lot and can

Age in months	Stage of motor development
Birth	Primitive reflexes only
1	Lifts up chin
2	Lifts chest up
3	Reaches for but does not grasp objects
4	Sits supported
5	Grasps objects
6	Sits on chair, reaches for and grasps objects
7	Stands with support
9	Stands alone but holding on
10	Crawls quickly
11	Walks holding one hand
12	Pulls up on furniture to stand
13	Crawls up stairs
14	Stands alone unsupported
15	Walks alone
24	Runs, picks things up without falling over
30	Stands on toes, jumps
36	Stands on one leg
48	Walks down stairs with one foot on each step

Figure 3.2 Average rates of motor development

now come down stairs backwards on their tummies. In playing, they can arrange toys on the floor, hold a pencil in the palm of their hands to scribble and can place up to three blocks in a tower. Infants love action songs like *pat-a-cake* and can turn several pages of a book together. They are also much more expert at eating with a spoon.

Intellectual development

Babies appear to prefer the sound of human voices as opposed to other sounds and soon learn to recognise their mother's voice. Within a few weeks, babies show an interest in human faces. Babies seem to be ready to feed and make relationships with carers soon after they are born.

Language

Infants begin to recognise words before they can talk or say words. At 6 or 9 months of age an infant may recognise and respond to words like 'clap-hands' and 'bye-bye'. Around the first year of life infants may produce **babbling** sounds that begin to sound like words. Some writers call these sounds pre-words, because sounds like 'nan' can mean 'I don't like that', or 'da' might mean 'I like that'.

Infants begin to say recognisable words at different ages. Many infants may say whole words as young as 1 year old, although others will take longer to develop their first word. By the age of 2 years most infants will combine two words together and begin to communicate their needs using the language they hear around them.

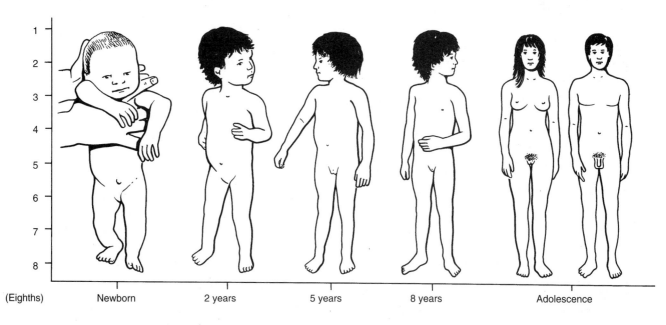

| (Eighths) | Newborn | 2 years | 5 years | 8 years | Adolescence |

Figure 3.3 Growth profiles from birth to adolescence

Although it can be 2 years or more before infants begin to combine words, infants do communicate with others using their face, their eyes and the sounds they make.

Thinking and memory

The development of thinking and memory is an important part of **intellectual development** (this is also sometimes known as **cognitive development**). This has been studied by many psychologists, perhaps the best known being Piaget.

To begin with, a baby will rely on in-built patterns for sucking, crawling and watching. A baby will adapt this behaviour to explore a wider range of objects. Babies explore by sucking toys, fingers, clothes and so on. In this way they are slowly able to develop an understanding of objects.

According to Piaget, thinking is at first limited to memories of actions. For example, babies will remember grasping a particular toy. If handed the toy again, they may repeat the action.

Piaget believed that infants could not understand that objects existed on their own. For instance, if an infant's mother left the room, the infant would be afraid she had gone for ever. Piaget thought that an infant was not able to understand that his or her mother still existed if the infant could not see, hear, smell or touch his or her mother. This stage is called the 'sensorimotor' stage and lasts until the infant is between $1^1/_2$ and 2 years of age.

At the end of the sensorimotor period, Piaget thought that infants could at last understand that objects and people continue to exist, even if you cannot see them.

However, modern research suggests that many 8-month-old infants can understand that people and objects still exist, even when you cannot see or hear them. Infants are more able than many people once thought!

Piaget's theory
(See Figure 3.4 below.)

Emotional development

Emotional development considers how people develop a sense of themselves as well as how they develop feelings towards others.

During their first year of life, infants can recognise the emotional expressions for happiness, distress and anger. It seems that, by 12 months of age, infants not only react to the facial expression of their carers, but they are also guided by the emotions they see on the faces on their carers. Studies show that infants behave differently with new toys depending on whether their mothers smile or look worried – infants will usually move towards a toy if mothers smile, but back away from it if their mothers look worried. It seems that infants come into the world with an in-built ability to recognise and to react to basic feelings in other people. Infants use this ability to attract attention and to build an emotional attachment with their carers.

Bonding

During the first 18 months of life, infants develop an emotional bond of love with their carers. This **bonding** process ties the infant emotionally to familiar carers. Some theorists think it is very important that children are not separated at any time from their mothers during infancy, so that this

Figure 3.4 Piaget's theory of child development

Stage of development	Age	Key issue
Sensorimotor	0–18 months/2 years	Children do not understand how objects exist
Pre-operational (pre-logical)	2–6/7 years	Children do not think in a logical way
Concrete operational	7–11 years	Children can understand logic if they can see or handle objects. Children do not fully understand logical arguments in words
Formal operational	11 years onwards	People can understand logical arguments and think in an abstract way

Infants need to experience a loving attachment with a carer

emotional bond can develop. Other theorists argue that an infant's main emotional attachment is not always with the mother; fathers and other carers are also important. Some theorists say it is the quality of love and care that matters most, and not whether carers ever leave their child (for example, to go to work). There is agreement that infants need to experience a loving attachment with a carer and, if this does not happen, then a child's social and emotional development will be damaged.

Sense of self

Young infants probably do not have a sense of being an 'individual' person. As infants grow they gradually learn they can influence their carers with the actions they make. At around 2 years of age, however, infants may develop the idea they are an individual person with a fixed gender. This idea of being a person is called **self-awareness**.

Social development

Social development explores humans' social behaviour and the social skills we need to communicate and make relationships with others.

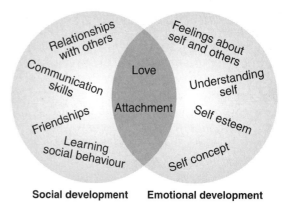

Figure 3.5   Social and emotional development overlap

Emotional development explores how we express our feelings and develop **self-esteem** and **self-concept**. It can be difficult to tell the two areas apart because these areas overlap (see Figure 3.5).

Our social relationships influence our emotional development and our self-esteem can influence our relationships with others. Hence such issues as love and attachment can be looked at from the point of view of both social development *and* emotional development. Infants soon learn to recognise their mother's voice and smell, and can probably recognise her face by 2 months of age. As we have already seen, infants try to attract attention by smiling and making noises.

At about 12 months of age infants often develop a fear of strangers and will protest if they are separated from their parents. After the first year of life infants feel safe with familiar family members if they have formed the necessary social bonds.

Talk it over

Do you think infants should always be looked after by their own mothers or fathers? Or can they be left with carers while their mothers or fathers go to work?

Early childhood

The term 'early childhood' does not have a fixed meaning in terms of age. Here, it is used to cover 2-12 years of age, although exactly where early childhood ends and adolescence begins is difficult to establish.

Physical development

18 months to 4 years

Toilet training usually starts between 18 months and 2 years. Children will show that they are ready, perhaps by telling the carer when they are wet or have a dirty nappy. At first, children will be dry during the day but will often wear a nappy at bedtime or be carried out during the night to sit on the potty.

Children are now very mobile and are able to run, to climb and to descend stairs. Kicking a ball is also now possible, but the skill of catching does not come until around 4 years old. A sense of balance is developing and children are able to ride a tricycle, move on tiptoe and climb on frames. At the end of this period, children can thread small beads to make necklaces, use scissors, copy shapes and draw recognisable people. The tower of bricks can now be built tall and straight, and painting becomes a favourite pastime. Tying shoelaces and fastening buttons are still a challenge for 4-year-old children.

4 years to 7 years

Children start school in this period, become increasingly co-ordinated in their physical activities and have generally lost their 'puppy fat'. By 5 years of age, head size and therefore brain size has just about reached adult size. The sense of balance is such that children can skip, jump off apparatus and learn to ride a two-wheeled bicycle. Growth in height and weight increase

Young children acquire a well-developed sense of balance by the ages of 6 or 7 years

steadily, but not as rapidly as before.

Both girls and boys are usually continent of urine or completely dry during the day and night by the time they are 5 years old.

8 years to 12 years

As milk teeth are replaced by permanent teeth and the jaws grow rapidly, facial features take on their permanent characteristics. Physical growth continues, muscles build and co-ordination is now such that musical instruments, swimming, football and gymnastics can be taken up with proficiency. Many girls begin **puberty** in this period, with the appearance of secondary sexual characteristics such as development of the breasts and sexual organs.

Intellectual development

Language

At around 2 years of age most children have started to speak, using two-word phrases such as 'Zoe sleep' (meaning Zoe wants to go to sleep). As children grow they start to use their own type of language pattern to communicate, such as 'I want drink' and 'the cat goed' (the cat has gone out). Young children of 2 or 3 years of age do not use adult language and it is probably best not to correct what they say. Children may go through stages of language development, such as the ones listed below:

1	Two-word statements	'Cat goed.'
2	Short phrases	'I want drink.'
3	Being able to ask questions	'What that?' 'Where is cat?'
4	Using sentences	'Jill come in and the doggy come in.'
5	Adult sentences	'I would like a drink and a piece of cake.'

By the age of 5 or 6 years, children can use adult speech and have a reasonable knowledge of words. However, children continue to develop their knowledge of words and their ability to understand and use speech throughout childhood.

Thinking and problem-solving

Between the ages of 2 and 7 years, most children learn to count and to explain how much things weigh. Young children do not always fully understand the logic involved in counting and weighing things.

Piaget called the period 2–7 years of age the '**pre-operational**' period. Pre-operational means 'pre-logical'. Young children may make decisions based on what things look like rather than the logic of counting.

Older children do not make the mistakes younger children do. However, 7–12-year-olds can often only understand logical problems if they can see what is involved. For example, you could ask a 9-year-old: 'Tanya is taller than Stephen, but Tanya is smaller than Tolu. Who is the smallest out of these three people?' Obviously Stephen is the smallest. A 9-year-old might not be able to work this out without looking at pictures of the people (see Figure 3.6).

Figure 3.6   Pre-operational thinking

Piaget called the period 7–12 years the '**concrete operational**' period, because older children can only work out logical problems if they can see 'concrete' examples to help them.

Emotional development

Children who have made good emotional bonds with a carer will start to feel safe getting to know other children or adults. All children take time to adjust to changes in their setting, and starting in a play group or school can still be stressful, even for 5-year-olds.

Self-esteem

Young children find it very difficult to explain feelings and emotions, but this may be because their language and thinking abilities are not fully developed. Research during the past 20 years suggests that young children do have the ability to understand and to respond to the feelings of others. Three-year-old children will sometimes try to comfort younger brothers or sisters who are upset. Children also need to feel they are valuable to their friends and family. Feelings of **self-worth** or self-esteem are very important if people are to grow up feeling emotionally secure.

As children grow, it seems they use their imagination to copy the behaviour of others. Children might copy the behaviour of parents or of people they see on TV. Children as young as $2\frac{1}{2}$ years can imagine dolls as talking and having wishes and feelings. By 4 years, children can imagine dolls as being characters who play with other characters. Because children can imagine the things they see others doing, they can also begin to imagine who they are and to start to create an idea of 'self'. More details of the development of self-concept are given in the section on self-concept later in this unit.

Social development

Children's attachment to parents and carers is just as strong as in infancy, but they no longer need to cling to carers. As children grow older they start to make relationships with other children and learn to become more independent. However, young children still depend very much on their carers to look after them, and they need safe, secure, emotional ties with their family. Emotional ties provide the foundation for exploring relationships with others.

Play

Play activities at any age can help us to:

⋄   develop our practical skills and abilities

⋄   develop social skills and relationships with others

⋄   make us feel better – play can provide a feeling of control or of relaxation.

Types of play
The word 'play' can cover many different types of activity. Children's play mainly involves exploring, practising, social learning and pretending (see Figure 3.7).

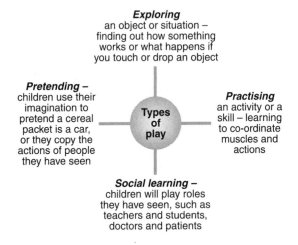

Figure 3.7   Types of play

The development of play
Before 2 years of age, children tend to play alone. At around 2 years of age, children may play side by side with other children, although they may still concentrate on their own activity. Children may start to share activities with other children at about 3 years of age. By 4 or 5 years of age,

children may play in small groups and follow activities or games with simple rules.

By 7 years of age, most children develop same-sex friendship groups. Children may often prefer being with their friends rather than doing other activities. By 10 years of age, friendship groups often share similar attitudes and values. Friendship groups start to have an influence on children's beliefs and behaviour during childhood.

Puberty and adolescence

By 'adolescence' we mean the age range 12-18 years (18 is the age when people are first allowed to vote and, by implication, take on adult responsibilities).

Physical development

Any time from 8 years old onwards, a girl's breasts start to enlarge. This happens well before menstruation and is usually the first sign puberty is starting. In both sexes hair starts to grow in the pubic area and under the armpits (and on the chest in boys), and there is a rapid growth spurt in an individual's overall growth.

Girls tend to reach puberty two years before boys (generally between the ages of 11 and 13 years). In both sexes there is rapid growth in the primary sexual organs (ovaries in girls and testes in boys) and also of the secondary sexual organs, such as the uterus (or womb), vagina and breasts and the penis and scrotum. Girls start to menstruate (the onset of menstruation is called the *menarche*), often irregularly at first with slight bleeding, and the first eggs are produced up to a year later.

Hormonal control

The changes outlined above are caused by hormones secreted by the pituitary gland. These hormones stimulate the production of **oestrogen** from the ovaries in girls and **testosterone** from the testes in boys. The oestrogen and testosterone cause the growth of the genital organs, skeleton, muscles and body hair. When ovulation is well established, a second female hormone is produced – progesterone. This is influential in causing glandular development in the breasts and the development of the uterine lining, whereas the action of oestrogen mainly affects the growth of these structures.

Figure 3.8   The body shapes of mature males and females

These hormones cause changes in body shape: a girl's pelvis widens, making her walk differently with swinging of the hips. She develops a curvy outline and fat is deposited under the skin and around the breast, giving her an hour-glass type of silhouette. Boys, on the other hand, retain their slim hips but they develop wide shoulders and a well defined muscle structure. Testosterone in boys is also responsible for the rapid growth of the voice box (larynx), causing the voice to 'break' and become deeper in pitch.

It is during puberty that boys catch up and overtake the girl's two years' head start in growth. Hence boys end up heavier and taller than girls, although there is a wide variation in mature adult heights and weights in both sexes. The tonsils and adenoids which protect against infection have steadily grown through childhood, but now surprisingly start to shrink quite rapidly. This is why surgeons are now reluctant to remove tonsils as readily as they used to in the 1950s and 1960s, because tonsils rarely give problems after puberty unless they are heavily infected.

The chart opposite shows a summary of how different parts of the body grow at different rates.

Intellectual development

Adolescents are able to imagine and think about things they have never seen or done before: they can imagine their futures and how they might achieve things in the future. Children are not able to plan and think ahead in this way.

Adolescents can solve problems in the same manner as adults.

Returning to the ideas of Piaget once more, Piaget called this stage of development the **formal operational** (or formal logical) period. Formal

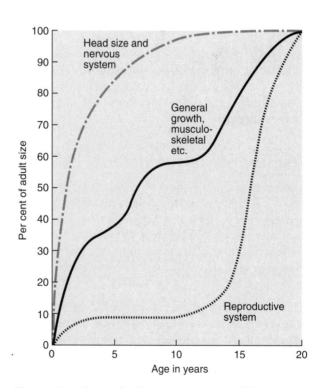

Figure 3.9 Some body systems have different growth rates

Figure 3.10   Solving problems in software writing involves the use of formal operational (logical) thinking

logic helps people solve problems at work and in daily life. Whereas children often make guesses when they have to solve problems, adolescents can often work things out logically (see Figure 3.10).

Although adolescents can reason in an adult way, they may often not know enough to make the right decisions. Decision-making skills are something we acquire throughout the course of our entire lives.

Emotional development

Adolescence is a period of rapid social and physical change. Some adolescents feel a loss of self-esteem as they transfer from school to work, and becoming independent of your parents can involve conflict and stress. Similarly, the search for love and affection from a sexual partner is not free of stress.

The psychologist Eric Erikson (1902–94) believed that a successful adult life depends on people developing a secure sense of their selves (their self-concept). During adolescence, people have to acquire a concept of themselves that will guide them through leaving home, obtaining work and perhaps learning to live permanently with a

partner of their own choice (see the section on self-concept later in this unit for further details).

Social development

Adolescents become increasingly independent of their families; hence friendship groups become more important than family for the development of social skills. This phase of development is called secondary **socialisation** (see Figure 3.11).

Figure 3.11   During adolescence friendship groups become more important than the family in the development of social skills

Between 12 and 18 years of age, most adolescents begin to explore their sexuality which includes testing out relationships and sexual behaviour with others. In late adolescence people begin to think about, or to take on, job responsibilities.

As young people take on adult roles they may experience trouble and conflict with their parents. This is the stage at which adolescents are trying to assert their adult **independence**.

Think it over   Which is more important to you, your family or your friends? If your parents wanted you to stop seeing someone because he or she was a 'bad influence' on you, what would you do?

Adulthood

In the UK people have the right to vote at the age of 18 years, so the age of 18 might be considered the age at which people achieve adulthood.

Physical development

People in their 20s and 30s are at the height of their physical powers and at their reproductive peak. In our 40s we tend to put on weight and become less physically active. Men may start to lose their hair and, in both sexes, grey hairs start to appear. The fine focussing power of our eyes declines so that most people become long-sighted and need reading glasses for close work.

Women continue to menstruate (i.e. are able to conceive children) until about the age of 45 years.

After this age they slowly reach the **menopause**, when menstruation stops. Consequently their bodies produce less of the hormones oestrogen and progesterone (which were formerly needed for menstruation), and hence the organs of the reproductive system shrink and the vagina becomes less elastic.

Both sexes lose skin elasticity, and this leads to wrinkles, particularly around the face.

Men can still father children into their 70s and even into their 80s, although sperm production and sexual performance will have declined.

Intellectual development

Intellectual skills and abilities may increase during adulthood if these skills and abilities are exercised. Older adults may be slightly slower when it comes to working out logical problems, but increased knowledge may compensate for slower reactions. Wisdom is perhaps our ability to use knowledge more effectively as we become older. Wisdom comes from many years of experience of life and so age may help people to make better decisions.

Emotional development

People's concepts of themselves and their feelings about their own self-esteem continue to develop throughout adulthood. During early adulthood many people struggle to develop the confidence they need to share their lives with a partner. Some may finally decide to live alone, feeling that partnership relationships are too demanding. People's experience of their family life as a child may strongly influence the expectations they have of a partner.

Research has suggested that adults often feel more confident and satisfied with their lives in their 30s and 40s than they did in their 20s. This may be because many young adults experience stress while they are trying to establish a satisfying lifestyle for themselves.

Some theorists have suggested that older adults may struggle to stay interested in and involved with other people after their own families have grown up. They may get into 'a rut' and withdraw from active social involvement. The menopause itself is not without its problems: women may become depressed and irritable, perhaps because there is now an imbalance in their hormones. Hormone replacement therapy is often advised to counteract these and other problems associated with the menopause.

Successful ageing, therefore, might be regarded as remaining involved with other people in an emotionally satisfying way.

Social development

Early adulthood is often a time when people continue to develop their networks of personal friends. Most young adults will have sexual relationships and may develop more or less permanent partnerships: marriage and parenthood might be important life events. Some may decide to have children later in their lives, prioritising their personal development and careers instead.

Many people experience stress when trying to cope with the demands of being a parent, partner and worker. Many individuals work long hours or even have more then one job in order to achieve a high standard of living. Going to work while maintaining a family home can create social and emotional problems. Adult life often involves trying to balance the need for money with the needs of partners and other family members (see Figure 3.12).

Older adults may find that, as well as pressures of work, they also have to provide support not only for their own children but also for their parents. Some older adults feel thay are sandwiched between different pressures. When their children leave home they may feel some of the pressures have been removed but may also feel they have lost part of their social purpose now their children have gone.

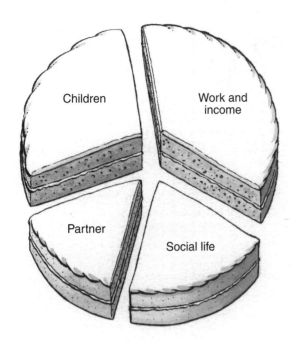

Figure 3.12 Adults have to work out how to divide up their time in order to meet different needs

? In one study, 59% of people in the UK stated they 'never seem to have enough time to get things done', and 21% stated they were very concerned about the amount of free time they had!

Although the official retirement age for men is 65 and for women 60, many people now retire in their 50s. Depending on how retirement happens to you – i.e. forced or taken out of choice – retirement can be regarded as a positive release from the pressures of work or as an end to your usefulness to others.

Old age

As we have already mentioned, most people retire by the age of 65, and therefore the period of life after the age of 65 is generally understood as old age. Most 65-year-olds do not see themselves as 'old', however. Some writers make a distinction between the 'young-old' (65-80 years) and the 'old-old' (80 years and over). Many 80-year-olds, however, still claim they are not old!

? Currently about 8% of the population is aged between 65 and 74 years. Seven per cent are aged 75 and over. By 2021, 11% of the population are expected to be between 65 and 74 years of age, with 9% over 75 years of age.

Physical development

The ageing process is subtle, and the changes it brings are so slow and so tiny we tend not to notice them. However, once we reach our mid 60s we begin to notice some changes:

- Our skin becomes thinner, less elastic, wrinkled and acquires blemishes.

- Our bones are more brittle and more likely to fracture, particularly in females.

- Our joints become stiffer and may become painful as the cartilage on the bone ends becomes worn away; the ligaments which reinforce our joints become more loose.

- Our height is reduced because the pads of cartilage that separate the vertebrae become compressed, causing the vertebrae to be closer together; the spine may also become more rounded.

- Our muscles are weaker and power is lost.

- Our sense of balance becomes impaired, particularly when turning round.

- Our taste and smell receptors deteriorate.

- Our vision can be further impaired because the lens of the eye starts to block light. This can be the forerunner of cataracts. Night vision is not as good as it used to be.

- We fail to hear high pitched notes, and we may become a little deaf.

- There is a general reduction in the skin's sensitivity, so that we are susceptible to burns and hypothermia. Hypothermia is when the body temperature falls too low. Some older people do not realise they are cold and this can be life threatening.

- The muscles that help food to pass down our digestive tract are weaker. Constipation is a common problem.

Older people's quality of life can be good

- The heart is less efficient at pumping blood around our body, so our bodily tissues do not function as well as they did.

- Our blood pressure is higher because the walls of the arteries have become hard and less elastic. This means we have a greater risk of strokes and brain haemorrhages.

- Nutrients from food are not absorbed as well as before. This can cause anaemia and vitamin deficiency diseases.

- Our breathing is less efficient because our respiratory muscles are weaker.

- Gas exchange in the lungs is impaired as the elastic walls of the alveoli become damaged.

- The glands that provide hormones (endocrine glands) do not function as well as they used to. The rate of metabolism (the chemical reactions in the body cells) is reduced due to a reduction in thyroxine (a hormone needed to regulate metabolism). Lack of effective insulin from the pancreas frequently leads to diabetes, particularly in elderly people who are overweight.

For all this apparently depressing list of ailments, older people can live healthy and fulfilling lives. People now live much longer than they used to and, with the right support and help, their quality of life can be good.

Intellectual development

In later life, some people may become less able at solving problems and coping with difficult, intellectual challenges. To some extent our mental abilities are influenced by our physical health: for example, poor blood circulation can interfere with the brain, causing difficulties with mental activities, such as problem-solving.

On the other hand, people who enjoy good health and who exercise their minds often retain their mental abilities and continue to develop their store of knowledge. Some older people seem to have an increased ability to make wise decisions and judgements. Even if thinking slows down, the opportunity to develop wisdom may increase with older age.

The risk of developing **dementia** or Alzheimer's disease seems to increase with age, but dementia is not part of normal ageing – most old people never develop dementia or Alzheimer's disease. There are different types of dementia but, in general, dementia can cause a range of disabilities:

- a loss of ability to control emotion

- difficulty in understanding other people

- difficulties in communicating and expressing thoughts

- loss of memory

- difficulties in recognising people, places and things

- problems with making sense of where you are and what is happening

- problems with daily living activities, such as getting dressed.

The reasons why some people develop dementia are not fully understood, but bad health habits such as persistent heavy drinking and smoking may increase the risk of dementia for some people. Other people may inherit a 'risk factor' for dementia because of their genetic pattern.

Emotional development

People's concepts of themselves continue to develop as life progresses. Some theorists have suggested that the main challenge of old age is to retain a strong sense of one's own self-esteem, despite the problems that can arise with age.

Older people may not only develop health problems but they can be stereotyped by other people, who assume they are less able than they are. Some older people may be at risk of losing their self-confidence and self-esteem because of the way others treat them.

Social development

Older people can lead very varied, different lives. Many retired people have a greater opportunity for meeting and making new friends than when they were working and bringing up a family. A network of family and friends can provide vital, practical and emotional support. Alternatively, health problems and impairments can sometimes create difficulties that result in social isolation.

> **Think it over**
> To lead a happy life requires a balance between an active social life and working to get money. What is the right balance between social activity and work during adolescence, early adult life, later adult life and old age?

Moral development

Finally, perhaps moral development deserves a section on its own, as our moral development changes throughout all the stages of our lives.

Children's beliefs about what is right and wrong are strongly influenced by the beliefs of the people they live with and mix with. The way children talk about what is right and wrong is influenced by their level of intellectual development. In 1976 a theorist called Kolberg published his ideas about how children and adults go through six different stages of moral thinking. These stages are outlined below:

1   *Punishment and obedience* Things are wrong if you get told off or punished for doing them. You should do what you are told because adults have power.

2   *Individualism and fairness* You should do things that make you feel good or get praised, and avoid things that get punished. It is important to be fair to everyone. For example, 'If I help you, you have to help me!', 'If I get pushed in a queue, then I have the right to push other people!'

There is a simple belief that everyone should be treated in exactly the same way. For example, if everyone gets the same food, this must be fair. Children at this stage will find it hard to work out that 'the same food' is not fair because it will discriminate against some people and not others. If everyone is given meat, this will be good for some people, but not for vegetarians!

3   *Relationships* As children grow older, relationships with others become important and children begin to think about the way they are seen by others. At this stage, children start to think about 'good' behaviour as behaviour that pleases others. Being good is about meeting other people's expectations of you. Ideas of loyalty, trust and respect come into children's thoughts and feelings. For example, a child might think 'I can trust my friend to keep a secret because they are a "good person".'

4   *Law and order* Adolescents and adults start to think in terms of a 'whole society'. Rules and laws are seen as important as they enable people to get on with each other. Being good is not only about relationships with friends and family, but also about relationships with people in general.

5/6   *Rights and principles* When adults reach these stages they decide what is right or wrong in terms of values and principles. Adults at these stages may argue that laws need to be changed. Adults take personal responsibility for working out what is right or wrong.

Social and economic factors

People do not all have an equal chance to develop their skills and abilities: some are born into a life that holds fewer opportunities than the lives of others.

In 1999 the DSS published a report called *Opportunity for All*. In this report the government states: 'Our aim is to end the injustice which holds people back and prevents them from making the most of themselves.' The government says its goal is 'that everyone should have the opportunity to achieve their potential. But too many people are denied that opportunity. It is wrong and economically inefficient to waste the talents of even one single person'.

The *Opportunity for All* paper also states that:

- The number of people living in households with low incomes has more than doubled since the late 1970s.

- One in three children live in households that receive below half the national average income.

- Nearly one in five working-age households has no one in work.

- The poorest communities have much more unemployment, poor housing, vandalism and crime than richer areas.

The report goes on to say that the problems which prevent people from making the most of their lives are as follows:

- *Lack of opportunities to work.* Work is the most important route out of low income. However, the consequences of being unemployed are far more reaching than simple lack of money. Unemployment can contribute to ill health and can deny future employment opportunities.

- *Lack of opportunities to acquire education and skills.* Adults who are without basic skills are substantially more likely to spend long periods out of work.

- *Childhood deprivation.* This is linked with problems of low income, poor health, poor housing and unsafe environments.

- *Disrupted families.* The evidence shows that children in one-parent families are particularly likely to suffer the effects of persistently low household incomes. Stresses within families can lead to exclusion and, in extreme cases, to homelessness.

- *Barriers to older people living active, fulfilling and healthy lives.* Too many older people have low incomes, a lack of independence and poor health. Lack of access to good-quality services is a key barrier to social inclusion.

- *Inequalities in health.* Health can be affected by low income and a range of socioeconomic factors, such as access to good-quality health services and shops selling good-quality food at affordable prices.

- *Poor housing.* This directly diminishes people's quality of life and leads to a range of physical and mental problems. It can also cause difficulties for children trying to do their homework.

Figure 3.13   Factors that affect whether people are able to make the most of their lives

- *Poor neighbourhoods.* The most deprived areas suffer from a combination of poor housing, high rates of crime, unemployment, poor health and family disruption.

- *Fear of crime.* Crime and fear of crime can effectively exclude people within their own communities, especially older people.

- *Disadvantaged groups.* Some people experience disadvantage or discrimination, for example, on the grounds of age, ethnicity, gender or disability. This makes them particularly vulnerable to social exclusion.

Figure 3.13 summarises some of the factors that stop people making the most of their lives.

Culture

The way we behave, the language we speak, the diet we eat, the way we dress and our lifestyles are all part of our **culture**. The concept of culture also includes those things that make one group of people different and distinctive from others.

Our culture gives us a set of rules or expectations that should help us to understand each other, and to know how to react in certain situations. Very often we do not even know we are working or living within a culture: we just 'do what is normal' and fit in. Because society is made up of various sorts of people, brought up in different circumstances or places, and following different beliefs and religions, different people's culture can vary enormously. We all tend to follow the way we were brought up and are perpetually influenced by the people around us. We follow a 'culture' (see Figure 3.14).

Within any culture there are a number of **subcultures**, which have slight variations from the main culture but which still adopt many of those things considered usual or 'correct' in the main culture.

Not everyone shares the same culture, and there are many different cultures in the UK. For example, travellers have made a different **lifestyle choice** from most other people. Most people live in a house and pay the charges and taxes associated with that. Travellers do not conform to this pattern. As a result of travellers frequently moving (either through choice, to follow work or because land owners and local authorities move them on), their children are moved from schools and benefits are difficult to claim (a fixed or permanent address is required to claim child benefit). Their health is put at risk because it is difficult to register with medical services when you are continually moving. The travellers' health, welfare and education consequently suffers. Travelling is a culture, an established way of life, and yet is not always recognised as such.

'This is the right way to live'

Gender

It was only in 1928 that women were granted the equal right with men to vote in elections. Before that, women were considered to have a lower social status than men. The assumption was that women should look after the children, do the housework, cook and tidy, and do light jobs. Men did the more valuable administrative, management and heavy labouring jobs such as building and loading ships.

Great changes have come about in the workplace and in the nature of family life since 1928. Women are now generally given equal

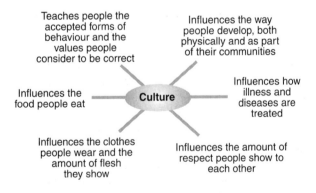

Teaches people the accepted forms of behaviour and the values people consider to be correct

Influences the way people develop, both physically and as part of their communities

Influences the food people eat

Culture

Influences how illness and diseases are treated

Influences the clothes people wear and the amount of flesh they show

Influences the amount of respect people show to each other

Figure 3.14   How our culture can influence us

opportunities in education and employment – and the Sex Discrimination Act 1975 makes it illegal to discriminate against women in education or employment.

However, current studies show that women's pay is as much as 17% lower than men's. Women still hold fewer top jobs and seem not to be promoted. Women far outnumber men in such jobs as nursing and primary school teaching – but, often, these jobs are not highly paid. Men often get the more highly paid jobs, even in areas of work dominated by women. When it comes to domestic work, men still generally do less of the child care, washing and cooking – although they may do more gardening and maintenance jobs.

> **Think it over**
>
> Women often feel there is a 'glass ceiling' which stops them achieving further promotion at work. They cannot really see what it is that is stopping them, but there is something there that prevents them getting on. In what ways might discrimination and stereotyping create an invisible ceiling that holds women back? For further information on these issues see pages 120–22.

Access to services

There is a great deal of evidence which shows that people on low incomes tend to have worse health than people who are on higher incomes. People who live in households where no one has a job often have worse health than people who are employed. Statistics show that people who stay poor or unemployed for most of their lives often have a shorter life expectancy than wealthier people.

The differences in health and length of life are probably caused by the problems people on low incomes face. Problems such as:

* poor housing, crowded living conditions, noise

* poor diet – unhealthy eating

* stress from crime, poor living conditions, debt

* negative thoughts about themselves (see the section on self-concept later in this unit).

Another problem is that people on low incomes and people who are unemployed may not be able to access services as easily as wealthier people.

Access to health services

There is some evidence that, in the past, doctors spent more time with wealthy and well educated people and less time with poorer people. However, most doctors probably do not intend to give a different quality of service to different people: it may be that more confident and well educated people can persuade doctors to take a greater interest in their needs.

There is some evidence to suggest that there are more health care professionals in wealthy areas than in poorer areas. This might have arisen because poorer areas are more difficult or more stressful to work in, or perhaps because it is easier to build new clinics and facilities in wealthy areas. Wealthier, employed people also seem to take more notice of health education advice and to live healthier lifestyles. Wealthy people can afford private health care and health checks.

What we can conclude from this is that being poor or being unemployed for a long period of time may mean not getting your health needs met as effectively as other people.

Access to education

Everyone has to go to school, and colleges are open to everyone. Even so, there is evidence to suggest that schools in wealthier districts often achieve higher standards and sometimes offer more opportunity to their students. Some parents even move house in order to send their children to what they think is 'a good school'.

Wealthy parents often pay for their children to attend private schools, because they think this will give their children better qualifications and skills, and also friends who will be able to help them with their careers.

The government claims it is trying to raise educational standards, to improve services for young children and to create special projects to improve facilities in deprived areas. This may help to even out some of these differences.

The family

The kind of family we are born into can have a great influence on our development.

What is a family?

A family is a social group made up of people who are 'related' to each other. This means that other people (society) recognise that this group is related. In British society, 'family' is the word used to describe groups where adults act as parents or guardians to children. **Belonging** to a family can have many advantages – family relationships can provide a safe, caring setting for children. Family groups can guide and teach children, and they can provide a source of social and emotional support for adults and older family members (see Figure 3.15).

Sociologists have identified four different types of family.

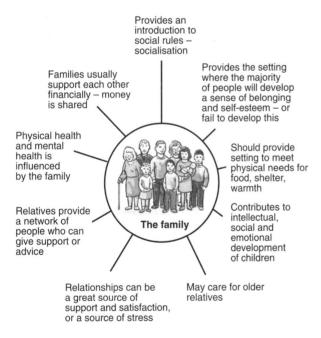

Figure 3.15   How the family can help people

Extended families

An **extended family** is where the parents, children and grandparents all live together or near each other so that they are in constant contact with each other. In England, between 1800 and 1900, many families lived in this way because everyone could help with the agricultural work that was necessary to make a living. The extended family can have many advantages. The parents might be able to work all day without worrying about who is looking after their children – the grandparents can help with this. If the grandparents need care, then the parents or even the older children can help. The extended family provides a network of people who can support each other. (See Figure 3.16.)

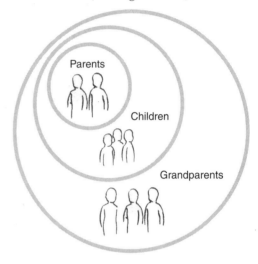

Figure 3.16   The extended family

Nuclear families

Many people now no longer live with their grandparents, and the term **nuclear family** is used to describe this smaller family arrangement, which usually consists of a husband, wife and their children. A nucleus is something's core: hence this family structure consists only of the core members of the family. Historically, the husband would go out to work, while the wife looked after the children while they were young.

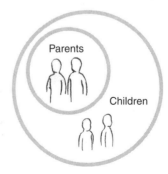

Figure 3.17   The nuclear family

Today, many couples no longer fit this description: often both parents have full-time work and the children are cared for by childminders, nannies or nursery services. Male and female roles have also been changing – men and women are now usually seen as equally responsible for household tasks. However, studies suggest that women still undertake the majority of child care and household tasks. See Figure 3.17.

Reconstituted families

Approximately one marriage in every three now ends in divorce, some people think this figure will rise. Many young people live together before marriage and have children, but there is evidence that a large number of these couples will also split up. Over a third of marriages each year are likely to be re-marriages, and about one million children live with a step-parent. Roughly a quarter of children below the age of 16 years might experience their parents divorcing.

The **reconstituted family** is where the couple are not *both* the parents of each child in the family. One partner might have been divorced from an earlier marriage and has now re-married to create a new family. Children from the previous relationships may be included in this new reconstituted family. Or one partner may have been single but is now married to a partner who has children from a previous relationship. (See Figure 3.18.)

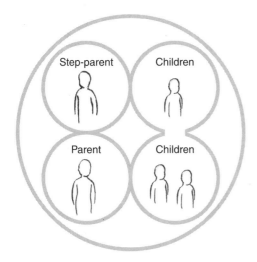

Figure 3.18 The reconstituted family

Lone-parent families

Nearly a quarter of all families with dependent children are now lone-parent families. Of families with dependent children, 21% are **lone-parent families** led by a lone mother, with just 2% led by a lone father.

While some lone-parent families may be well off, many are disadvantaged. Studies suggest 70% of lone parents have incomes equivalent to the poorest 10% of couples with dependent children. Many lone parents rely on benefits or receive low wages.

The type of family a child lives in can change: an extended family can turn into a nuclear family if the grandparents die or move away. Families can become 'reconstituted' if one partner leaves and is replaced by a different person. Few people can guarantee a family style for life. When people leave their partners, divorce or die, a lone-parent family can be created. If the remaining parent finds a new partner, the lone-parent family becomes a reconstituted family. The same child might live in different family structures during his or her childhood and adolescence. (See Figure 3.19.)

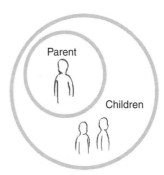

Figure 3.19 The lone-parent family

A 1999 report predicts that, by 2010:

- fewer people will form families
- there will be a 33% increase in lone-parent households
- there will be a 55% increase in people living alone
- about 22% of women aged 45 years will not have had children.

How family circumstances can influence lifestyle

CASE STUDY – Anil and Rick

Anil is 8 years old and was born into a family where his parents had good jobs and enough money for lots of toys, books and computers. Anil learned to play on his father's computer when he was only 3 years old. This has helped him to learn. Anil always has someone to talk to at home because he lives with his sister and grandparents in a large house. The family is happy and Anil can go out on his cycle and play with friends in the local park. Anil's family are not afraid of crime in their neighbourhood. Anil is doing very well at school. He has many friends and enjoys school. Anil does not miss school very often.

Rick is 8 years old and was born into a family where both his parents had difficulty in finding work. Because Rick's parents cannot get jobs, there is not much money for toys, books or computers. Rick lives in a crowded block of flats on a housing estate. Rick's mother does not let him out to play because she is afraid of the crime and drug-taking that takes place on the estate.

Rick's mother has periods of depression when she does not talk to Rick. Rick is often unhappy because he has few friends and he gets bored indoors. Rick often gets colds and misses a lot of school. Rick is like one third of children who grow up in low-income households. He does not have the same chance of a happy and wealthy life as Anil.

Questions

Look again at Figure 3.13: 'Factors that affect people making the most of their lives'.

1   Can you see how Rick's story fits with the problems there?

2   Can you see how Anil has been 'born lucky' in that he does not have these problems?

3   What sort of future lives will Rick and Anil have?

Anil's story continues later in this unit, but Rick may not have such a happy life.

Friends

Friends are very important; they can help us to do practical things, such as housework, find a job, repair a car and so on. Friends can also help us emotionally. Friends can listen to us and protect us if we feel stressed. Friends can help us sort out our worries and help us have an interesting and enjoyable life.

Think it over

List all the things you do over a week, such as going to school or college, going out in the evening and so on.

How many of these things could you do without friends?

Friends help us with:

- practical tasks
- emotional needs
- social life.

People without friends will probably have a more difficult and less enjoyable life than people with many friends.

Friends influence the things we believe and the values we hold. As we have already seen, early in life our family influences us (and this influence is called *primary* or *first* socialisation). Socialisation is the process through which we learn social values.

As we get older, such things as school, television and friends come more and more to influence our beliefs and values (this is known as *secondary* socialisation). Our friends can influence the way we behave, and the friends we have during adolescence can have a long-lasting influence on us. If we mix with friends who think it is important to try hard at school, we will probably try hard too. If we mix with friends who take drugs, we may copy what they do.

Low-income housing

People on low incomes often have to live in poor-quality or high-density housing. This kind of housing can mean that people have some of the stresses shown in Figure 3.20. People on low incomes may have trouble paying for maintenance or looking after their homes. Some of the risks connected with poorly maintained housing are shown in Figure 3.21. See Unit 2 for further details on environment and housing.

Ethnicity

For many people, their race is of vital importance as it enables them to understand who they are. Race is not easy to define, however. In the past, people believed that different races were somehow biologically different, but it is now known that it is almost impossible to define racial groups in terms of genetic differences or features

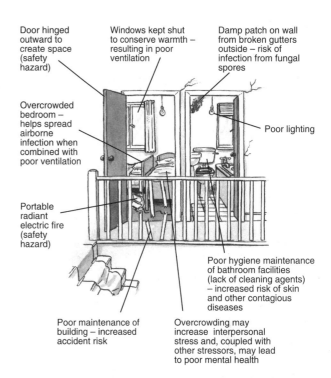

Figure 3.21 Poor housing may contribute to a wide range of hazards to health and social well-being

to do with skin colour or physical appearance. Nevertheless, people do classify themselves and are classified by others in terms of the social and cultural groups to which they belong. A person's culture, religion, style of dress, way of speaking and so on may lead to classification in terms of ethnic group.

A key way people distinguish themselves is in terms of being Black or White: some talk in terms of Black, White or Asian groups of people. However, there is no single Black culture, and no single White culture.

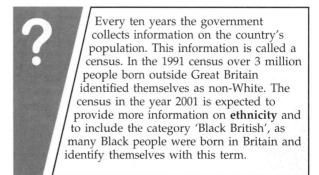

Every ten years the government collects information on the country's population. This information is called a census. In the 1991 census over 3 million people born outside Great Britain identified themselves as non-White. The census in the year 2001 is expected to provide more information on **ethnicity** and to include the category 'Black British', as many Black people were born in Britain and identify themselves with this term.

Figure 3.20 The stresses that can arise from low-income housing

Since 1965, laws have been in force in the UK to prevent **discrimination** on the basis of race. The Race Relations Act (passed in 1976) set up the Commission for Racial Equality, which seeks to investigate cases of discrimination based on racial or ethnic group. Despite the law and the powers of the Commission, however, there is evidence of inequality between White and Black groups in the UK. Black and Asian people are more likely to be victims of crime than are White people. In general, people from ethnic minority groups are less likely to achieve top professional and management positions than White people.

Unemployment rates vary between Black and White groups but, generally, rates of unemployment are higher for Black people than for White people. In 1991, 12 per cent of White men were unemployed compared with 22.6% of non-White men. Among White women, 7.4% were unemployed, compared to 18.4% on non-White women.

Many Black and Asian people feel that services and employers discriminate against them. A report in September 1998 by the University of Warwick found that four out of five young Black people felt that race relations were getting worse. Employment opportunities and police behaviour are seen by many Black people as the key areas where they are discriminated against.

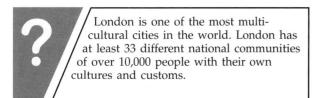

London is one of the most multi-cultural cities in the world. London has at least 33 different national communities of over 10,000 people with their own cultures and customs.

Isolation

Isolation means not having contact with other people.

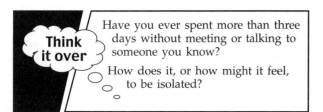

Think it over

Have you ever spent more than three days without meeting or talking to someone you know?

How does it, or how might it feel, to be isolated?

Social isolation

Social isolation is when you are out of contact with friends, colleagues or family, even though there may be many strange people nearby. People who move home or who go into hospital may feel social isolation for a short time until they get to know new people. Social isolation can cause people to feel lonely, depressed, worried or worthless. Extreme isolation may make people want to give up on life and to die. Many older people experience social isolation.

In 1997, more than 55% of women and 30% of men over the age of 75 years lived alone. Living alone does not create social isolation, but some people who live on their own do lose touch with friends and family. Some older people have no children or grandchildren to visit them because:

- some older people may never have had children

- some children and grandchildren live too far away, or are too busy to visit their grandparents

- some children die before their parents, or become ill and unable to visit.

Older people may also lose contact with friends because:

- hearing, visual or mobility problems can make it difficult to go out to meet people

- friends may develop disabilities which make it difficult for them to communicate, visit or phone

- illness and stress can make them withdraw from company and become isolated

- as time goes on, their friends may become ill and die.

Some older people ask for home care or other social services because they are lonely and isolated.

Discrimination

Discrimination means telling things apart – knowing the difference between things that appear similar. It is quite all right to discriminate between, say, a sandwich filling you do not like and one you do. Telling things apart is a vital part of life – if we did not do it we would not be able to live independently.

However, discriminating against people has a different meaning; it does not mean 'telling them apart'. While it is important to realise that all people are different – with different life experiences – discriminating against people means giving people an unequal service or treatment because of their differences.

If an employer did not want to appoint a woman to a job because she might leave to have children, for example, the employer would be illegally discriminating against her. This would be discrimination because she was treated differently from a man who might want to start a family. A man in this situation might be appointed; but the woman is treated unequally.

Common forms of discrimination are based on people's race and culture, gender, age, disability and sexuality. Discrimination is serious because it can:

⋄   damage people's sense of self-esteem and value

⋄   block people from making the most of their lives

⋄   lead to verbal and physical abuse

⋄   cause people not to receive quality care and services.

Stereotyping

Life is very complicated for everyone but sometimes people try to make life easier by considering certain groups of people to be 'all the same'.

For example, a younger person meets an 80-year-old who has a problem with his or her memory. The younger person has seen someone like that before on TV – it hence becomes all too easy to think that 'all old people are forgetful'. This would be **stereotyping** – a fixed way of thinking about a group of people (see Figure 3.22).

People may make assumptions based on stereotyped thinking. For example, a carer working with older people might say 'I'll just go in and wash and dress this next one – I won't ask

Figure 3.22   Stereotypical thinking

what she would like me to do because she's old and old people don't remember – so it does not matter what I do'. Stereotyped thinking like this may cause us to discriminate against people.

When people say 'all women are' or 'all Black people are' or 'all gay people are' they will probably go on to describe a stereotype of these people. Skilled caring is when we are interested in people's individual differences; stereotyping lumps people together as if they were all the same and stops us from being good carers.

Stereotyping people and discriminating against people can arise from all sorts of apparent differences between people:

⋄   Able people may discriminate against disabled people.

⋄   White people may discriminate against Black people.

⋄   Men may discriminate against women.

Some common bases for discrimination are shown in Figure 3.23. It is always wrong to discriminate against and to stereotype people. Discrimination causes different amounts of damage depending on how it happens.

Figure 3.23   Some of the common causes of discrimination

Common differences that lead to discrimination: Gender, Social class, Age, Sexuality, Disability, Culture, Race

Think it over

Imagine you go into a shop with friends. You have money to spend and you are fit and able. But the shop assistant appears not to like you and does not really want to serve you – how will this affect you?

Now imagine you are alone and in pain lying on a hospital trolley. The nurses appear not to like you and not really to want to help you – how will this affect you?

Consider how you would feel in the situations described in the 'Think it over' above. In the first instance you would feel angry and you would probably choose never to use that shop again! In the second instance you would feel vulnerable. The care staff have power, perhaps your life is in their hands – yet they do not want to give their best. You would probably feel frightened, worried and devalued.

The power people have can make a difference as to how much harm an act of discrimination can cause.

Income

Economic factors that influence people's development include the **wealth** and **income** families have. Wealth includes:

- savings, in banks or building societies
- the value of your home if you own it
- shares, life assurance and pension rights
- any other property that belongs to you.

Income is the money you get each week to live on. Income mainly comes from:

- wages you are paid for working
- profits from your business if you are self-employed
- benefits paid by the government to help people
- money from invested wealth, such as interest on bank accounts
- money raised through the sale of property you own.

Wealth is not shared out evenly in the UK. The poorest half of the population only own 8% of the country's wealth and property. The top 1% of the richest people own 19% of the UK's wealth. The richest 10% of the population own 50% of the wealth. If wealth was a cake, Figure 3.24 shows how it would be shared out.

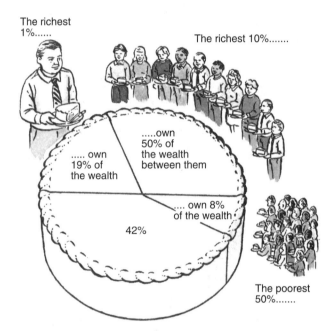

The richest 1%...... own 19% of the wealth. The richest 10%....... own 50% of the wealth between them. 42%. ....own 8% of the wealth. The poorest 50%.......

Figure 3.24   The UK wealth cake (based on 1995 figures reported in *Social Trends 1999*)

Income is what really matters to the vast majority of people: your weekly income enables you to pay for your house or flat, and feed and clothe yourself. Wealth, on the other hand, might matter to others. For example, some older people have a low income but own their own house; if necessary, they could raise money on their home through special remortgage schemes or even sell up and move into leased or rented accommodation. Whichever is most important, both wealth and income increase the chances of a person making the most of his or her life.

Availability of money for essential items

Over the last 20 years most people have enjoyed an increasing standard of living. People have better cars, better entertainment and better computers. Many people have more money to spend than ever before. However, studies show that the poorest people have missed out on this prosperity: a 1999 report states that one third of British children live in **poverty** in households that do not have enough income to give children a good start in life.

> **?** In 1995, four out of ten households in the UK felt they could not afford to go on holiday, even for one week.

How much money you have affects where you live and how you live. It affects whether you eat the right diet, whether you can go on holiday, or have savings to fall back on if you lose your job. Low income can cause the kinds of problems shown in Figure 3.25.

Figure 3.25   Some of the problems a child belonging to a low-income family may face

Availability of money for non-essential items

Budgeting is a difficult skill to learn. Some people never get the hang of it and constantly find they run out of money before they have bought the essentials or paid the bills. Budgeting is really a matter of setting priorities for the income you have (such as paying the rent or the mortgage, feeding and clothing the people in the household), and then seeing what is left to spend on other things.

Try it out

Think about how much money it costs for your family to live for one week. Talk to others in your family and complete the box below, listing everything you and your household spend. Make a guess as to how much each area costs.

1 Essentials	Cost	2 Important things	Cost	3 Luxuries	Cost

Some things are not essential, but they are not luxuries either – they are just things you have become used to having and would rather not do without. Where would you put a magazine or a bar of chocolate – what about a CD player? You could live without them!

See if you can budget for your household for the whole week. Do not forget things which must be paid for, but you do not notice, for example:

⋄ light and heat

⋄ water rates and council tax

⋄ mortgage repayments or rent

⋄ house insurance.

Think about food, clothing and other consumer goods.

Could you cope if you lost the main source of income for the household? Where could you start to cut back if someone lost his or her job?

Spending money on non-essentials is a way of 'treating' yourself or other people. You might buy yourself clothes to feel special in, or save up for a holiday. Even a bar of chocolate or a magazine after a hard day can make you feel that life is not just a daily grind to pay the bills. When you are short of money, with no spare cash to spend on non-essentials, this can be depressing and can affect your self-esteem.

Effects of social and economic factors on health

Poverty, a lack of wealth and low income can influence how long you live. For the past 30 years, studies have shown that, in general, poor people have more sudden illnesses and more long-term illnesses than more successful, wealthier people. More babies are born dead to poor mothers than to wealthier mothers. More infants and children born to poor parents die before 14 years of age than children born to wealthier parents. On average, poor people die sooner than wealthier people.

Studies have also shown that people who own their own home have fewer illnesses and live longer, on average, than people who rent their homes. People who have steady employment enjoy better health than people who are unemployed; and mothers from poor housing areas are likely to have low-birth-weight babies. Exactly why a lack of money is linked with

CASE STUDY – Mrs Grahame

Mrs Grahame is a widow aged 83 years. She lives in a second-floor flat in a large house. She has travelled widely in her life – she and her husband lived all over the world. She was the only daughter of a teacher and qualified as a teacher herself, but she has never worked. When living in India and in South America she had servants to run the house and she is accustomed to giving orders.

Since her return to England following the death of her husband 12 years ago, life has not been easy. She does not qualify for a state pension and her savings are gradually being used up.

Friends from the church she attends are getting worried about Mrs Grahame – none of them have even been told her first name. She always feels the cold and seems to be getting more frail. She refuses to see the doctor and last week she shut the door in the district nurse's face, saying 'Mind your own business'.

Questions

1 Why do you think Mrs Grahame is refusing help?

2 How will Mrs Grahame's social and economic problems influence the way she feels about herself?

Figure 3.26 How social and economic factors can affect people's lives

Development	A child born into a low-income family – negative factors	A child born into a high-income family – positive factors
Physical	Poor diet – too much fat and sugar	Balanced diet with the right protein, fibre, vitamins and minerals
	Restricted exercise	Healthy activity
	Overcrowded and dangerous home – risk of accidents and illness	Safe, healthy environment
	Stressful home and community environment (too dangerous)	Safe, relaxed home and community both during childhood and adulthood
Intellectual	Few toys, few books, poor electronic equipment	Toys that help with learning – good learning packages
	Parents stressed, spend little time with children	Parents or childminders spend time with children
	Low expectations of school	High expectations of doing well at school
	Parents have bad experiences of school and do not help	Parents help children with school work
	Low educational achievement and low-paid work as an adult	High educational achievement and better paid work
	Poor skills and worries about coping	Good social skills and education to cope with life's problems
Emotional	Stressed parents may not spend enough time making relationships with their children	Less stressed parents may concentrate on relationships with their children
	Children may feel not as good at things as other children	Children learn to feel successful and competent
	Low self-esteem	High self-esteem
	Trouble finding a good job	Feelings of success at work
	Feeling out of control of own life and feeling controlled by others – unable to choose own lifestyle and place to live	Able to choose own lifestyle and place to live and feeling in charge of own life
Social	Restricted opportunities to play with others	Access to playgroups and social groups
	Friends that hate school encourage others not to try	Friends that value educational achievement and career success
	Friends may be stressed or unable to help	Access to an adult network of friends who can help with work and other needs

shorter life and worse health is not fully understood.

Isolation, loneliness and poverty all have effects on the way a person might think, feel and behave. Poverty can have long-term effects on health. Not having enough money to keep warm or to eat properly will damage your health, especially if you are more vulnerable. Even thinking you might not have enough money may cause stress. Older people, young children, pregnant women and people who are already ill are often at greater risk of long-term damage to health than other people.

Social and economic effects on employment prospects and education

There are many reasons why people decide to discontinue education. To stay in education after the age of 16 years requires interest, ability, opportunity and income. Without these, further or higher education can be very difficult. Even though students aged 16 years and over do not have to pay for further education, a family might rely on a 16-year-old to go out to work to bring some money into the home. Some students help their parents financially, or pay rent to their parents to make ends meet.

The level of education an individual achieves can affect the type of employment they may get. Often, jobs with low-entry qualifications are not highly paid. This can affect the standards of living an individual might be able to reach, the type of housing and diet he or she can afford and so on.

Poor housing and poor neighbourhoods are often found in areas where there are few job opportunities – because many people have no work the area becomes poor. Good job opportunities tend to attract people who will buy property and improve it. Being born in an area of poor housing may sometimes mean that a child will have fewer opportunities for work than a child born in a more wealthy area.

? For each week's work, the average solicitor earns four times the wages of a waiter or waitress (1998 figures).

In many ways, work, housing and education opportunities are often linked. Poor job opportunities may lead to poor neighbourhoods and cause people to believe that education is a waste of time and effort.

Self-esteem

Social and economic forces have far greater effects on your life than just where you live and what you can afford to buy. They affect the way you think about yourself and your life in terms of your feelings about whether you are a success or a failure. If you are struggling to look after yourself because your income is low, you might choose to try to learn new skills, or attempt to find somewhere cheaper to live. If you cannot provide for your family, you might feel you have failed them, as well as yourself. Self-esteem (how you regard yourself) is vital to enable individuals to cope with the everyday pressures of life (self-esteem is covered in more detail in the following section of self-concept).

The way social and economic factors affect people's lives is summarised in Figure 3.26.

Think it over

Suppose you won a lot of money on the lottery. How would your win influence the way you think about yourself? Would it increase your confidence? Would you feel more important?

Self-concept

Self-concept means the way we think about ourselves (see Figure 3.27). How we acquire our self-concept is a very complicated process. However, a simple way of understanding self-concept is to see ourselves as having four 'selves': physical, intellectual, emotional and social. Using this idea of self-concept, you could fill in the questionnaire which follows.

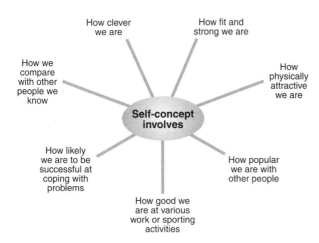

Figure 3.27   Self-concept

The self-concept questionnaire

Thinking about yourself in relation to other people you know, how would you rate yourself on the questions below ? Give yourself a mark out of five for each question; one if you are not very good, five if you are very good! Use the chart in Figure 3.28 to record your scores. For example, if you think you score 3 for question 2 under 'Your physical self', shade in the score 3 under the number 2 in the diagram. Be careful to shade in the correct part of the circle – physical self in the top left-hand quarter!

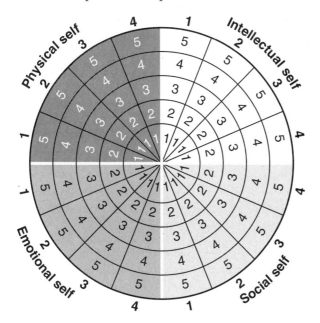

Figure 3.28   Scoring the self-concept questionnaire

Your physical self

1   How attractive are you?

2   How healthy are you?

3   How fit are you?

4   How good are you generally at sport and physical activity?

Your intellectual self

1   How good are you at maths and number work?

2   How good are you at communication and English?

3   How good are you at scientific thinking?

4   How good are you at art, music and general academic work?

Your emotional self

1   How good are you at guessing what other people are feeling?

2   How good are you at understanding your own feelings?

3   How good are you at getting on with other people, including people who are sad or angry?

4   How good are you at making yourself concentrate on work you know you have to do?

Your social self

1   How good are your relationships with members of your own family?

2   How easy do you find it to mix and make friends with new people?

3   How good and satisfying are your close friendships?

4   How good are your relationships with other students or colleagues?

When you have shaded in all your scores on the chart to the left, your 'self-concept pattern' will emerge. Compare your pattern with others. Can you work out why there might be differences or similarities between you?

Some people may have a high score in each area, which might mean they have a very positive self-concept. Other people may have a low score in each area, which might mean they have a poor or negative view of themselves. Many people will rate themselves high on some areas but low on others. This is quite normal: our self-concepts are usually mixed – we think we are good in some ways but not in others. Each person develops his or her own special view of him or herself. This is because of the experiences people have had as they have grown and developed.

Why is self-concept important?

Some psychologists consider our concept of ourselves as being the most important thing in life. Developing and keeping a clear sense of self has been described as 'the goal of living at any age'.

Our view of ourselves is important because it can:

* motivate us to do things or stop doing things, for example, doing well at school or at sport

* create a feeling of social confidence or cause us to feel anxious with other people

* mean that we experience happiness or unhappiness from life experiences

* help us lead a successful and enjoyable life, or can lead us into trouble and difficulties in coping with life.

If we think we are good at school or work we will probably enjoy going to school or work. Our concept of ourselves will make us want to be there. If we think we are not good at school or work, we may not want to go there. The way we think about ourselves influences what we do and how we feel (see Figure 3.29).

Think it over

Do you avoid activities or situations you are not good at or that you feel you cannot cope with? Can you work out why it is you avoid these activities or situations? (It may help if you look back at the scores you gave yourself on the self-concept questionnaire).

Figure 3.29   Our skills at dealing with the problems of others vary

Self-concept development
Can you change your self-concept?

Yes – because our knowledge of ourselves changes as we go through life. But we cannot change our **self-confidence** or motivation by just wishing things to be different. Our self-concept develops and changes because of the experiences we have. Therefore we should perhaps seek out new life experiences that might help us to change our self-concept.

How does self-concept develop?

When we are born we do not understand anything about the world we are born into – we do not know we are an individual person. The beginnings of self-awareness may start when an infant can recognise his or her own face in a mirror. This happens somewhere about $1^1/_2$–2 years of age, when an infant begins to demonstrate that he or she is different from other people.

From this point on, children begin to form ideas about themselves. Children are influenced by the

Figure 3.30 The development of self-concept

Age	Stage of development
$1^1/_2$–2 years	Self-awareness develops – children may start to recognise themselves in a mirror
$2^1/_2$ years	Children can say whether they are a boy or a girl
3–5 years	When asked to say what they are like, children can describe themselves in terms of categories, such as big or small, tall or short, light or heavy
5–8 years	If you ask children who they are, they can often describe themselves in detail. Children will tell you their hair colour, eye colour, about their families and to which schools they belong
8–10 years	Children start to show a general sense of 'self-worth', such as describing how happy they are in general, how good life is for them, what is good about their family life, school and friends
10–12 years	Children start to analyse how they compare with others. When asked about their life, children may explain without prompting how they compare with others. For example: 'I'm not as good as Zoe at running, but I'm better than Ali.'
12–16 years	Adolescents may develop a sense of self in terms of beliefs and belonging to groups – being a vegetarian, believing in God, believing certain things are right or wrong
16–25 years	People may develop an adult self-concept that helps them to feel confident in a work role and in social and sexual relationships
25 onwards	People's sense of self will be influenced by the things that happen in their lives. Some people may change their self-concept a great deal as they grow older
65 onwards	In later life it is important to be able to keep a clear sense of self. People may become withdrawn and depressed, without a clear self-concept

environment and culture they grow up in; they are also influenced by the relationships they have with their family and friends. As children's ability to use language develops this will also affect how they can talk and how they can explain things about themselves.

People develop an increasingly detailed understanding of their selves as they grow older. A general outline of the development of self-concept is given in Figure 3.30.

The self-concept we have when we are very young is influenced by our family or carers. Hence primary-school age children are influenced by the adults around them but as we grow older our friends gradually take their place. As adolescents we often compare ourselves with others and choose a particular set of friends accordingly.

Our self-concept doesn't usually settle down until we are ready to go out to work full time or until we plan to leave home and live with a sexual partner. Until this time of life it may be that we

experiment with ideas of what we may be like and what we may be good at. Adult commitments perhaps force us into making decisions about ourselves. It could be for this reason that some people may not be able to explain their self-concept clearly until they are in their early 20s.

A clear sense of what you think you are like and what you think you are good at may be necessary if you are to be happy, confident and successful at work and in love (see Figure 3.31).

Influences on self-concept
Age

Age makes a big difference to the way children describe themselves and to the way adults think about their lives. Our self-concept grows and changes as we grow older. Some general differences in self-concept between various age groups are shown in Figure 3.32.

Figure 3.31   The development of our self-concept

Figure 3.32   The differences in self-concept between various age groups

Age	Expression of self-concept
Young children	Self-concept limited to a few descriptions, for example, boy or girl, size, some skills
Older children	Self-concept can be described in a range of 'factual categories', such as hair colour, name, details or address, etc.
Adolescents	Self-concept starts to be explained in terms of chosen beliefs, likes, dislikes, relationships with others
Adults	Many adults may be able to explain the quality of their lives and their personality in greater depth and detail than when they were adolescents
Older adults	Some older adults may have more self-knowledge than during early adult life. Some people may show 'wisdom' in the way they explain their self-concept

Appearance

Somewhere between 10 and 12 years of age, children start to analyse the ways in which they are like or not like others. Children start to work out how they fit in with others – do they look good or not, are they popular with others or not?

The physical shape of our body, our height, weight, hair, eyes and skin colour all influence how we see ourselves and how we think about ourselves. Many people believe there is an 'ideal look' which they should resemble. If we think we look good then we have a positive **self-image**. If we think we do not look attractive we may have a negative self-image. A negative self-image may make us feel bad or have feelings of low self-esteem.

What looks good depends on the culture and the beliefs of the people around us. Take body shape as an example. One hundred years ago, being a bit fat was considered attractive in European culture. A woman who was very thin was seen as poor and unhealthy; a fat man was considered to be someone who was successful. This began to change in the 1950s and 1960s, when looking

Figure 3.33   Former 'ideal' body shapes

young and thin became the goal to aim for. By the 1980s, children's toys promoted the 'Barbie-doll' look. While very few people ever looked like these ideal shapes, people judged themselves as attractive or unattractive in relation to these shapes (Figure 3.33). Nowadays, TV, videos and magazines tend to promote 'fitness' as beauty. Both men and women should have some muscle but little fat.

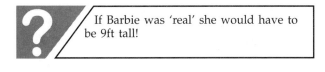

If Barbie was 'real' she would have to be 9ft tall!

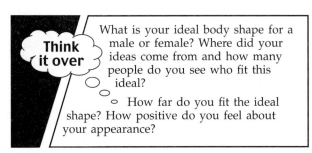

Think it over

What is your ideal body shape for a male or female? Where did your ideas come from and how many people do you see who fit this ideal?

How far do you fit the ideal shape? How positive do you feel about your appearance?

The way you look may indicate you belong to a particular group of people: your hairstyle, dress and behaviour can give other people clues about your gender, age group, wealth, lifestyle, beliefs and culture.

Adolescents usually copy their friends' style of clothing: they often have a need to dress differently from their parents and the 'older generation'. This helps to give them a sense of independence from their families.

Clothes, hairstyle, make-up and body shape are seen differently by different people. No one looks attractive to everyone. What you see as attractive may be attractive because of your own age, culture and lifestyle. The important issue is to feel positive about the way you look. We can easily develop a negative self-image if we do not understand the way other cultures or personal beliefs influence other people's opinion of our appearance (see Figure 3.35). A poor self-image may cause us to lack confidence or to feel depressed about our relationships with other people.

Culture

Different people have different customs and ways of thinking. Your family or the community where you grew up may have different beliefs and expectations from other families and communities. All these things influence the way we think (see Figure 3.34).

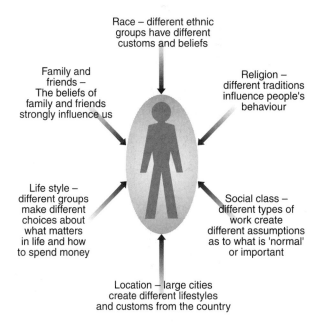

Figure 3.34   Some of the things that may influence our customs and ways of thinking

Figure 3.35   No one has the same views about our appearance

People develop different beliefs, values, habits and assumptions because of the social experiences they have had. We call this range of influences 'cultural influences'. Our culture can influence how we understand ourselves because different cultures create different ideas about what is normal or what is right. Sociologists call these ideas **norms**. Some of the norms that influence what we think of as right or wrong are described below.

Different norms about food

Different religions forbid different foods. For example, Muslim and Jewish people do not eat pork, and most Hindus and Buddhists do not eat any meat.

Different ethnic traditions surround the way food is eaten. White Europeans will eat cold food, such as bread, with their fingers but there are limits on eating hot foods with fingers. Asian customs allow certain 'hot foods to be eaten with the

fingers'. Most white British people will not eat snails, frog legs, snake, insects, dog or cat. Snails and frog's legs are eaten by other Europeans. Some other cultures do not restrict what can be eaten.

Different norms about education

Children born into middle-class families are likely to be taught they must do well at school and get a good career. Children in other families may not be brought up (or socialised) in the same way. Asian and South East Asian cultures often stress the importance of educational achievement.

Different norms about behaviour

Some families and communities may emphasise norms about keeping appointments, never being late and being organised for work. Other families may emphasise the importance of relationships and being honest with your friends. Different communities have different views on such issues as drug taking. Some families see using drugs as a very serious crime; others do not think this way.

Different norms about sex, marriage and gender roles

Different religions, families and communities have different beliefs about marriage. Many religions teach that sexual behaviour is only acceptable within marriage. Some communities believe that women who become pregnant outside marriage bring shame on their family. Other families and communities believe that sexual behaviour is entirely a matter for individual free choice.

What you think of as being important, or right or wrong, will be influenced by the norms of the people around you. What you eat, how much you care about education, your attitude to drugs and sex, will be influenced by your culture. Culture will also influence how you think about and judge yourself. For example, whether you think you are good or not will be influenced by your culture. Your self-esteem (how you feel about yourself) will be influenced by cultural beliefs about what is right and wrong.

Developmental maturity

Infants may begin to understand they are a person – that is, different from other people – before 2 years of age. Infants, however, do not have a self-concept. Concepts are ideas we acquire when we start to use language effectively.

Children develop language skills very quickly between the ages of 2 and 6 years, and the way children describe themselves changes as their language skills develop. At $2^1/_2$ years a child may be able to tell you whether he or she is a boy or girl, but may not be able to use other concepts such as how tall or how old he or she is.

By 5 years of age children have developed enough language skills to be able to describe themselves in terms of how tall they are, their age and some of their physical skills, such as: 'I can climb. I can ride my bike.'

The development of language and thinking skills alters the way we can understand who we are. By the age of 8 or 9 years, children may be quite good at describing themselves. They may say

something like: 'My name is Paola. I live at number 58 Birchill Drive. My mum's name is Gina. I have dark hair. I have lots of friends. I like swimming. I love my mum. ' Children between 8 and 10 years can describe lots of things about themselves, but their concept of self may still be limited to simple factual things, such as where they live and the colour of hair they have. Ten-year-olds do not usually have the intellectual skills to answer a question such as 'describe your self-concept'. By 16 years of age, adolescents have usually developed an ability to understand themselves in much greater depth.

A 17-year-old might say: 'Who am I? Well, I'm an individual. I know who I am but it's difficult to put into words. What can I tell you? I'm not going to tell you everything – well, I'm a vegetarian – well most of the time. I am an Aquarian but I don't believe what they say in the 'Stars'. I like mixing with people – even weird people. I love clubbing and I go out a lot. I'm slow to make my mind up – I can't make my mind up about my boyfriend and don't know what I think about relationships.'

What a 17-year-old says is different, not only because he or she is older but because his or her intellectual ability to think about self has developed since he or she was 10. Children may only be able to think in very simple factual ways. Adolescents can often think in more abstract and complicated ways. Adolescents start to think about what they believe: is it right to eat meat or not? What kind of relationships should people have? Adolescents choose causes and groups to belong to – they choose the issues that make up their self-concept.

Adolescents also start to think about what they are thinking! For instance, a child might look at themselves in a mirror and think: 'That's my face.' An adolescent will have more thinking skills – an adolescent might look at him or herself and think: 'I'd like my hair to be different – I want to change how I look – I'll get my hair done at the weekend, just like my friends.' Adolescents not only recognise themselves but they can also use their thinking skills to plan, to change and to develop into whom they want to be.

Physically, people are fully developed by 19 years of age. Some modern psychologists claim that our thinking abilities continue to develop and mature across the adult life-span. People in their 30s and 40s are often able to feel confident and make better judgements about important issues. Some people may become wiser and more able to understand themselves with age. Life experiences and **developmental maturity** may help people to develop more knowledge about themselves as adult life progresses.

Environment

Self-concept is influenced by the people we mix with as we grow up. It is also influenced by the media (TV, computer games, the Internet, newspapers, magazines, etc.). Sometimes the word 'environment' is used to mean all the influences on us which come from other people and from society. When environment is used in this sense it can mean relationships with others, culture, education, gender roles and the media.

Environment can also be taken to mean simply the area where we live. Where we live may influence self-concept in two main ways. First, we may live in a local culture that will influence us and, secondly, the housing we live in may make us feel safe and supported or it may make us feel stressed.

Local culture

The people who live in our neighbourhood may have special customs, habits and ways of speaking. They may include us in social activities. There may be temples, mosques, churches, clubs, centres, village halls or other places where we go to meet friends. We may feel at home in the local culture of our neighbourhood. Many people feel they belong to their own special community. Many develop a concept of themselves as a person who belongs in one special location.

Some people's self-concept would include the geographical area where they grew up. Some people say things like 'I'm a Londoner' or 'I'm a Northerner'.

Housing

People in the top social classes tend to live in more expensive housing and in areas that have good facilities for leisure and education. People with lower incomes may live in more densely occupied housing areas. They may feel they have little choice about where they live. People with money

can choose what kind of house to buy and where to live. The ability to choose where you live may help to provide a sense of control and of self-worth. If you feel 'trapped' where you live, this feeling may lower the value you place on yourself.

Poor-quality or high-density housing can create an environment that has;

- stress-creating noise
- pollution from traffic or local industry
- overcrowding within properties, thus reducing privacy and increasing stress
- poor access to shops and other facilities
- petty crime, again leading to stress
- health hazards as a result of poorly maintained property, such as damp, cold and safety risks.

If you live in an environment that is stressful, it may mean you do not feel valuable or important – you may have low self-esteem. People who live in pleasant areas generally feel more confident and positive about themselves – and their housing may contribute to higher self-esteem.

Education

Our idea of who we are is strongly influenced by our experiences at school. Between 5 and 16 years of age, most people will spend more than half the time they are awake at school, doing homework or meeting with friends from school. Our experiences at school influence our concepts of how attractive, how popular, how skilled and how clever we are. Later experiences at college or university can also confirm or change what we think about ourselves.

Education influences us because:

- we mix with other people and may compare ourselves with them
- the tasks we have to do influence our beliefs about what we are good or bad at
- we may learn theories and ideas that help us to understand our lives.

Mixing with others

Throughout our lives the people we mix with influence what we think is right or proper to do. If we mix with people who think it is important to get good marks in exams, then we will be

Figure 3.36   The expectations people have of us can affect how much we achieve

influenced to think that exams matter. If we mix with people who think that exams do not matter, then we may not bother to try. If people often want to involve us in their social activities, we may begin to feel confident and positive about ourselves. If people often ignore us, we may begin to feel we are not very valuable.

CASE STUDY – Jai's story

Jai is 15 years old. He is trying very hard to learn a new subject at school and wants to pass his exams. Jai wants to do well because he knows this would please his family. Jai's family believe it is important to do well at school and Jai has been brought up (or socialised) to believe that school work matters.

At first, Jai does not know whether he will be good at the new subject. He works with a small group of other students and realises they do not know what to do. Jai is able to help the other students and thinks to himself: 'I could be good at this.' Two weeks later Jai gives a task in for marking. When Jai gets the task back, it is praised as being clever and well written. Jai is pleased. At break time Jai asks his friends how they got on. Several of them say they found it difficult. Jai thinks: 'I am good at this.' Jai now begins to find the new subject enjoyable and he looks forward to lessons.

Jai feels good about the new subject and therefore he can imagine ways of writing his assignments. He enjoys talking about the subject. Being good at the subject becomes part of his way of thinking about himself. If something goes wrong in a future assignment, Jai will not give up. He has learned he is good at this work and that he will do well in the end.

Jai thinks of himself as a success. Other people think he is good at the subject, so he thinks he is good at it.

Questions

1   What might have happened to Jai's self-concept if he had failed at the work?

2   How has other people's praise or criticism influenced your own beliefs about your own abilities?

The way other people act towards us influences our self-concept.

Success and failure

What teachers, parents and friends expect from you can influence how good or bad you are at school subjects. If children are labelled as 'likely to do well', there is evidence they often do go on to achieve. People's expectations can have a big influence on children. If the people around you expect you to fail, then you are more likely to do badly (see Figure 3.36).

> *'Nothing succeeds like success.'*

A sense of self that says we are good at something can motivate us to spend time and effort working hard to achieve good results. If we think we are 'no good' we will probably give up easily.

The stages that lead to achievement

Sometimes people like Jai have positive experiences that work in the following way:

Background: family and friends value achievement, and therefore:

1   the child is motivated to try

2   first experiences are positive

3   the child begins to develop confidence

4   the child receives praise for achievement

5   the child decides he or she is good at the subject

6   the child enjoys doing the subject

7   the child's self-concept includes 'being good at the subject'.

Outcome: a positive self-concept keeps the individual motivated.

Not everyone develops a positive view of his or her ability during his or her time at school or college. Very often the steps outlined above do not happen. Hence people can lose their confidence or get to dislike subjects when they do not feel successful. Some people are not motivated right from the outset because they do not believe that study matters.

Good experiences can lead to a positive self-concept. Just wishing or imagining you are good is

Think it over

How have the ideas about self-concept contained in this book influenced your own understanding of your life story so far?

What are the most important influences that have affected your own self-concept?

If there were no books, computers, school, or college, would you still have developed an understanding of self-concept?

not usually enough. People have to experience positive experiences in order to develop a positive self-concept.

The power of ideas

Understanding such ideas as socialisation, labelling and expectations can help us to understand the influences that have affected our own achievement and performance. Education influences what we think and how we think, and education can help us to develop new ways of understanding ourselves because it gives us new ideas.

Gender

Very early in life children seem to be able to classify themselves in terms of gender – children know whether they are a boy or a girl. Along with ethnicity and age group, gender is a major social influence that affects how we understand ourselves. There are different social expectations of men and women. Men are expected to dress, think and behave differently from women. Men are similarly expected to have different interests and habits from women.

Sociologists see being a man or being a woman rather like having a role in a play. People have gender roles or 'parts' they have to perform throughout life. Fifty years ago in Britain, gender roles or 'parts' were quite rigidly different for men and women (see Figure 3.37).

The nature of society has changed dramatically over the last 50 years, and gender roles have also changed. Both young men and women now expect to go to work and most people do not expect to fight in wars. The Equal Pay Act 1970 and Sex Discrimination Act 1975 brought in the principle that women are equal to men. Before

Figure 3.37 Differences in gender roles in the 1950s

Men	Women
Expected to work full time	Expected to support husband by undertaking household duties (washing, cleaning, cooking, etc.)
Expected to provide money to pay for housing and family	Expected to care for children and older relatives, as necessary
Expected to organise household and to do household repairs	Expected to look after and clean home. Might do part-time or light work to improve household income if no child care work was needed
Expected to fight for country if necessary	Might take on men's work if country went to war and there were not enough men to work in the factories

these Acts, men were often thought to be more valuable employees and were paid more money just because they were men! Furthermore, at the beginning of a new millennium people are no longer assumed to all be heterosexual. The pattern of family life has altered, and many individuals may not live as couples with children during their early adulthoods.

Despite all the changes some gender role differences still exist. Jobs that involve working with young children or cleaning are still mainly done by women. Jobs that involve engineering, building or vehicle repair are still mainly done by men. Women's pay is still 17% lower than men's (on average, between the two groups). Men tend to achieve the top-ranking (highest paid) jobs more often than women.

When it comes to self-concept, women are likely to think differently from men. Career success,

work and making money are standards men may judge themselves against more than do women. More women than men see a successful life in terms of good relationships. Hence the gender roles of 50 years ago still influence how people think of themselves today.

Relationships

In some ways 'we are all other people'. Our idea of self develops because of the way other people talk to and act with us. Self-concept is strongly influenced by the quality of the emotional relationships we make with others. Throughout life, relationships affect how successful and happy we are, and our self-esteem is likely to be influenced by our relationships with others.

If you were about to bring a new baby into the world you would want to make sure the child enjoyed most of the positive things listed in Figure 3.38.

The way we communicate with and get on with other people directly affects our self-concept. We will copy the cultural views of our friends and family. We will judge our appearance in terms of the people we mix with. We may take on a male or female gender role because of the influences of friends, family and the local community.

Our friends, family, relatives, teachers and community are similarly influenced by:

- the local environment

- their education and developmental maturity

- their cultural background and gender roles

Think it over

In your household, who mainly tends to do the following tasks, or are they shared equally between men and women?

- shopping
- ironing clothes
- washing clothes
- cooking
- cleaning rooms
- cleaning bathrooms and toilets
- earning money to pay bills.

Do you still see some types of activity as part of a male or female role? How does this influence how you think about yourself?

Does your behaviour fit a 'gender role'?

Figure 3.38 The effects of personal relationships at different stages of a person's life

Good relationships can produce:	Poor relationships can produce:
Infancy Secure attachment between the infant and parents A rich learning environment A safe, loving environment which meets a child's emotional needs	A failure to make a secure or safe emotional attachment between parents and the child Neglect, rejection of the child
Early childhood A secure home from which to develop slowly Parents who can cope with the stressful behaviour of young children Friendships with other children	A stressful home situation Neglect or rejection of the child Inconsistent attempts to control a child Parents who become angry or depressed because of the child Isolation from other children
Later childhood Membership of a family or care group Socialisation into a culture Friendships with others at school Increasing independence from parents A feeling of being confident and liked by other people A feeling of being good at things	Stress and change if parents fight each other or separate No clear feeling of belonging with a group or culture Limited friendships Feelings of not being liked by others Feelings of not being good at anything or not as good as others
Adolescence Independence but still with the support of the family A network of friends, a sense of belonging with a group of friends A culture shared by friends A positive environment that has opportunities for the future	Conflict and fighting with parents and family Few friends, feeling depressed and rejected No feeling of belonging with other people No clear sense of who you are The feeling that life is not worth much
Adulthood A network of friends and family who help and support you A secure, loving, sexual relationship Good relationships with work colleagues The ability to balance time pressures between work, partner and other family relationships A feeling of being secure and safe, with other people to help you	Feelings of isolation, loneliness, rejection and no feeling of belonging with friends No support Changing relationships No social protection from stress Low self-esteem
Old age A network of family, friends and partner to provide emotional support Control of own life A sense of purpose	Few friends, no social support No social protection from stress Isolation No sense of purpose

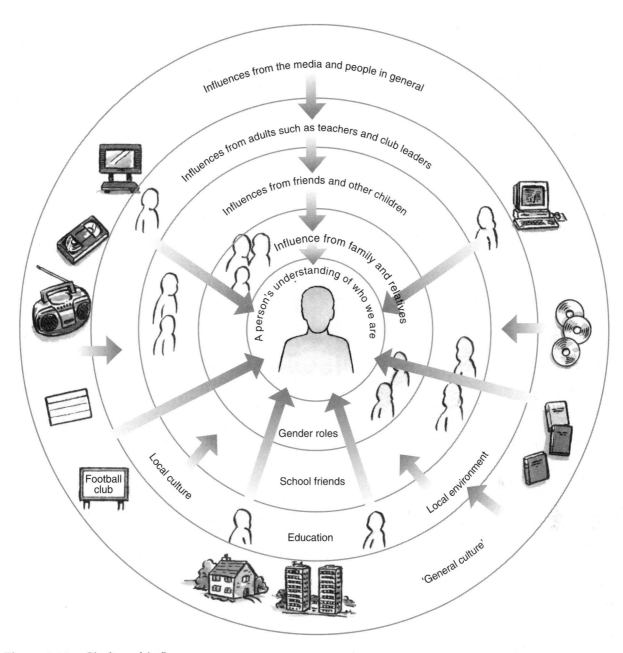

Figure 3.39 Circles of influence

- the wider influences in Western culture, including newspapers, TV, radio, the Internet, computer games and so on.

It is possible to think of these influences working at different levels, like the circles in Figure 3.39.

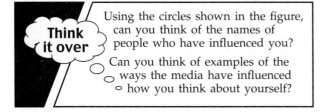

Think it over

Using the circles shown in the figure, can you think of the names of people who have influenced you?

Can you think of examples of the ways the media have influenced how you think about yourself?

Life changes

Living a successful life involves coping with **change**. Many changes during life are predictable. We know they will happen and sometimes we even choose to make the changes. Some examples of predictable change are:

- starting a new school
- growing up and going through puberty
- starting a new job
- leaving home

◇   marriage
◇   changing job
◇   retirement.

Some types of change are unexpected or unpredicted. These include:

◇   the birth of a new brother or sister
◇   physical injury or illness
◇   divorce
◇   the death of a friend or relative
◇   redundancy.

Positive and negative effects of change

Change usually involves some level of stress. When people choose to change, for example, when they get married or start a new job, the stress may be experienced as excitement. People may feel 'butterflies in their stomach' on their first day at work, but they may also look forward to meeting new people and learning new things. Some changes, such as the death of a friend, are experienced as being negative and these will usually cause people to feel very stressed.

Some life events change us for ever. **Life changes** involve some stress because change can cause:

◇   a sense of *loss* for the way things used to be
◇   a feeling of *uncertainty* about what the future will be like
◇   a need to *spend time* and/or *money* and/or *emotional energy* sorting things out
◇   a need to *learn* new things.

Changes in location
Going to school

Some people are taught at home because of travelling problems or personal needs. Most people, however, go to school and many will remember their first day.

Starting school can involve a sense of loss. This might be the first morning your mother and

CASE STUDY – starting school

David is a black 4-year-old who is starting nursery school. Until now he has always been at home with his mother. He has played with other children many times in his home and also when his mother visited friends. David is an only child. He has a close, loving relationship with his mother.

David's first reaction to school was one of shock – there were so many other children and it was noisy. He had always looked to his mother for guidance, but she was not there and he was on his own. David had been told all about school, but he could not really understand or imagine what it would be like. Another adult who looked very different from his mother was trying to get him to join in a game. David felt frightened and lost. David cried for his mother and told staff he wanted her. A kind teacher who looked a little like his aunt spent time with him and he felt better.

Later in the day, David enjoyed some food and joined in making music with the other children. When his mother came to collect him he was relieved. He did not really feel safe until she appeared. Now he felt tired, but important. He had been to school, he had learned about music and his mother made him feel everything was all right and safe again. This was a real adventure!

Questions

1   Can you remember starting or changing school?

2   Did you feel a sense of uncertainty, tiredness, excitement or fear when you went through this change?

3   Were your experiences positive or negative?

family have left you to cope with lots of other people on your own. You might cry because you miss them. You might also feel uncertain. Where are the toilets? Whom should you speak to? What will happen if you do not like the food?

Starting school can also be stimulating and positive. Some children feel it is exciting to meet new people. They might find school interesting and be proud they are 'grown up' enough to start school activities. Starting school can be a positive experience, involving increasing independence – it all depends on how each child is helped to cope with the change.

David's needs might be summarised as follows:

- *Physical*: David needed food and drink and to be active. The shock and excitement made him feel tired.

- *Intellectual*: David had lots of new things to learn. He needed to feel he was doing well.

- *Emotional*: David was used to feeling safe with his mother. David lost this feeling of safety. David did not know what to expect and was scared.

- *Social*: David needed to feel welcome – to get on with, and be included in the activities of, others.

The teachers and helpers at David's school would understand young children's needs for food, drink and rest. They would use their communication skills to help David understand new activities. Teachers would understand his emotional stress at being parted from his mother. They would do their best to meet his social needs by including him.

CASE STUDY – going out to work

Rahim is 18 years old and has successfully completed an information technology course at college. He wants to design software in the future but decided he would like to get some experience of working first. Rahim wrote over 30 applications to companies in his area asking for work. Most of his applications were unsuccessful and Rahim was very disappointed. Eventually he was successful in getting a temporary job at a local company helping to design spreadsheets and doing data entry.

Rahim felt very anxious on the first day. He wanted to do well and prove he was 'smart'. Rahim did not know what to expect. He did not know what they would ask him to do or how other people would treat him. Rahim was worried about the older workers in the company. Some might see him as a **threat** because he was young; others might be racially prejudiced against him.

On his first day he was warmly welcomed by a senior member of the company who suggested he work closely with a 38-year-old manager. Rahim was nervous at first but soon found his new boss was easy to get on with. During his first day Rahim began to feel the job would be interesting and that the people were OK to work with. At the end of the day Rahim felt exhausted but looked forward to the weeks ahead.

The staff understood how difficult it is to start a new job and therefore they helped him and gave him a guide or 'mentor' to teach him all the new things he needed to know. Anxiety turned into excitement. Rahim felt he could cope. Rahim felt the effort to learn a new way of working would be worthwhile.

Questions

1 What might happen if staff are not sensitive to the needs of new people?

2 How effective would Rahim's work be if he felt that he did not get on with others?

CASE STUDY – leaving home

Sarina is 21 years old and works near the centre of the city. Sarina has lived at home up until now but has decided to share a flat with a friend who works with her. Sarina will have her own room and will share the costs of renting and running the flat with her friend.

Before deciding to move out, Sarina had to do a lot of work to find a flat that was suitable and not too expensive. She spent over a month looking around at different flats. Sarina also had to sit down to work out what the running costs would be and how much money she would need to live on her own. She was shocked to find out just how much of her wages would have to be spent on rent, heating and food. Sarina also had to be sure she could trust her friend to look after their flat, pay her share and that they would get on together.

Sarina is sad to be leaving her parents, but she wants to be independent, to invite friends round and to do what she wants without having to involve her parents all the time. The new flat is also much easier for travel to work.

Sarina is anxious about the money and about getting on with her friend. Sarina is not used to looking after her own home – she will have to learn to do housework and plan her own meals and weekly budget.

Questions

1   How might Sarina's move to independence influence her self-concept?

2   Can moving home have an influence on a person's sense of who he or she is?

Rahim's needs might be summarised as follows:

- *Physical*: Rahim's first day was stressful so Rahim became tired.

- *Intellectual*: Rahim had a lot to learn. He was interested and excited by his new job.

- *Emotional*: Rahim was worried about racial discrimination. He was afraid of failure and rejection. Rahim's self-esteem and self-concept were threatened.

- *Social*: Rahim had a need to be included, to become a part of the staff team.

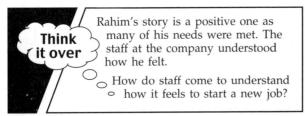

Rahim's story is a positive one as many of his needs were met. The staff at the company understood how he felt.

How do staff come to understand how it feels to start a new job?

Sarina's needs might be summarised as follows:

- *Physical*: searching for a place to live and worrying about money will make her feel tired.

- *Intellectual*: there are a lot of things to learn in order to run your own home.

- *Emotional*: Sarina is sad to be leaving her parents, but excited at being independent.

- *Social*: Sarina will have a new social life when she lives in the new area and can invite her friends round to her flat.

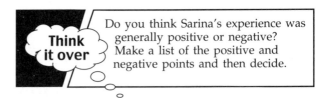

Do you think Sarina's experience was generally positive or negative? Make a list of the positive and negative points and then decide.

Relationship changes

Throughout life, emotional relationships are of central importance to human health and happiness. Research suggests that people who have strong loving relationships are happier and healthier than those without. People who are widowed or divorced are more likely to take time off work and to see the doctor more often than married or single people. Death rates for newly divorced or widowed people are higher than for people of the same age who still have partners.

Relationships with family and friends are also important. Talking with friends, family and colleagues may help protect us from the stresses we might otherwise face in life. Parents protect us in early life, while adult relationships with partners and friends help us to cope with change in adult life. Relationships with family, friends, work colleagues, neighbours and the wider community are important because of the benefits they provide. These benefits are summarised in Figure 3.40.

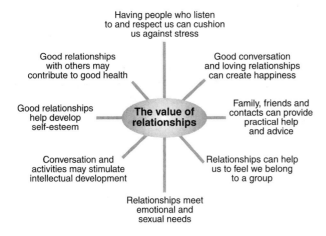

Figure 3.40 The value of relationships

Some changes in relationships, such as marriage, are seen as positive because they may increase many of the benefits relationships bring. Other changes may be viewed less positively because they take these benefits away.

The birth of a new brother or sister

Gaining a new brother or sister changes our relationships with our parents and other family members. Children's reactions to a new member of the family can be very varied, and reactions differ depending on how old a child is and how large the family is. Very often children have mixed emotions. Children may feel pleased they have a new brother or sister, but they may also feel jealous that their new sibling (brother or sister) gets more attention from the others. Some of the positive and negative feelings associated with gaining a new brother or sister are listed in Figure 3.41.

Marriage

In Britain, marriage is the legal union of one man to one woman. Gay and lesbian couples cannot currently be registered as married. Some other cultures permit a husband to have more than one wife or a wife to have more than one husband, but the legal definition of marriage in Britain restricts marriage to one man and one woman.

Many heterosexual couples live together without marrying – some may go on to marry after living together for some years, but about half of all couples who live together do not go on to marry each other. Current trends suggest that perhaps one in five people will never be married during their lives.

Figure 3.41 The positive and negative feelings associated with gaining a new brother or sister

Positive	Negative
Feeling important because you can care for the new infant	Feeling rejected because your parents seem to spend more time with the infant
Feeling pleased because there are more people in your family group	Feeling you have been replaced in the family and are not important
Feeling valued because you are the older child	Feeling your attachment to the family and parents is threatened
Making a relationship or attachment with your new brother or sister	Feeling you are in competition with your brother or sister

Marriage involves a commitment to live with a partner permanently. It ties the financial resources and the networks of family relationships together. Marriage is a big change in life and it can involve moving house and leaving your family. This may cause a sense of loss. Many people feel some anxiety about getting married: are they marrying the right person, will they get on well together, what will living together for ever be like?

Learning to cope with married life takes a lot of time, money and energy. Living with a partner involves learning about his or her needs and ways. For some people marriage is the most positive change that can happen in life. Other people regard it as involving a loss of freedom, or even as entering a relationship where one person dominates or exploits the other.

Talk it over

Discuss with your friends how positively or negatively you view marriage. What rating would you each give it on a five-point scale from one (very negative) to five (very positive)?

Divorce

At present, one in three marriages is likely to end in divorce. In the 1950s many people stayed married despite being unhappy with their partners. In the past, it was often difficult to get a divorce and there were likely to be serious problems over money and finding somewhere to live following divorce, particularly for women.

Divorce is much more common nowadays, but many people who divorce go on to re-marry. Each year, over a third of marriages are likely to be re-marriages. Nearly a quarter of children in Britain may expect their parents to divorce before they are 16 years old.

Although many people experience divorce negatively, it may often be better than living in a stressful situation. Sometimes people develop a deeper sense of self following divorce. Agencies such as Relate provide counselling services to help people to understand the emotions involved in partnerships. Counselling may help some people to decide whether it is best to divorce or not.

Parenthood

Becoming a parent involves a major change in life. Many parents experience their relationships with their child as an intense, emotional experience. There may be strong feelings of love and a powerful desire to protect the child. However, becoming a parent also involves losses – parents can lose sleep because the baby wakes them up, and they may find they cannot go out very easily – they lose touch with friends and their social life. Parents can lose money because they either have to pay for child care or give up full-time work to care for their child. Parents can lose career opportunities if they stay out of full-time work to bring up a family. These losses can sometimes place a relationship or marriage under stress – sometimes a parent can even become jealous of the love and attention a child receives from the other parent.

Becoming a parent can involve some anxiety about the role of being a parent: 'Will the baby be healthy?', 'Is the baby safe?', 'Am I being a good mother/father?' New parents usually seek advice from family, friends, doctors and health visitors. Parenthood involves a great deal of pressure on time, money and energy. A new infant will need nappies, clothes, toys, food, cot, high chair, car seat and so on. An infant needs a lot of attention. Carers will need time and emotional energy to care for the child. Parents often need advice on caring skills – there is new learning involved in being a good parent and always much to learn about the child as the new relationship develops.

Retirement

The nature of work is changing rapidly. Many people will be self-employed or temporary workers in the future, and retirement may become very flexible with some people effectively retiring in their 40s and others continuing to take on work in their late 60s and 70s. Retirement can represent a

Think it over

Retirement provides a mixture of positive and negative possibilities. If you were to talk to people who have been through retirement, what would they say were the main problems and the main advantages?

How positively or negatively would they rate retirement?

major change for people who have worked in a demanding full-time job and then stop working completely.

A sudden break from full-time work might cause a feeling of loss. Work roles influence self-concept, so a person's self-concept and self-esteem can change following retirement. People may lose their routine and perhaps their work friends when they retire, and some people may not be prepared for the leisure time they have and be unsure what to do with their time each day. Some people say that retirement makes them feel redundant – they are no longer of use to anyone. People who have to live on the state pension alone may experience a loss of income. Some older people live below the poverty line.

On the positive side, people with private pensions and savings often have the time and money to travel, study or take up hobbies and so they thoroughly enjoy themselves. Some people see retirement as a time of self-fulfilment, when they harvest the rewards of a lifetime's work. Retirement can lead to greater freedom and the opportunity to spend more time with family, relatives and friends.

The death of a friend or relative

People can lose their partners at any stage of life but, as couples grow older, the chances one person will die increase. **Bereavement** means

CASE STUDY – bereavement

Nathan had been married for 22 years when his partner unexpectedly died of a heart attack. They had been very close. When Nathan was first told about the death he showed little reaction. Friends had to persuade Nathan not to go into work the next day. Nathan had said it would give him something to do – take his mind off things. Later, at the funeral, Nathan said he felt frozen inside and that he did not want to eat. It was some weeks later that Nathan said he felt better because he could talk to his partner, sitting in a chair late at night. Nathan admitted that he never saw his partner, he just felt a presence.

As time went on, Nathan said he felt he could have done more to prevent the heart attack; if only he had noticed some signs, if only they had not smoked. Nathan felt angry with their local doctor. His partner had seen the doctor only two months before. Surely, if the doctor was any good, they should have noticed something! On occasions, Nathan just became very angry and bitter about how badly everything had gone. Perhaps he was to blame?

Months later, Nathan explained he had sorted his life out a bit. Whereas his partner had used to organise things, he had now learned to cope alone. He explained that he spent time with a close friend – ' shoulder to cry on', as he put it.

After a year and a half Nathan still misses his partner but he now says the experience has made him stronger: 'It's as if I understand more about life now. I feel – if I could cope with this loss – well, there isn't much I can't cope with.' Nathan has now become involved with the local voluntary support group for people who are bereaved. He says helping others has helped him: 'It has given me new meaning and purpose in life. I think everything in life has a purpose – things are meant to happen to you. I had a good life before and now I've got a new life to lead.' Nathan says that 'life feels OK now'.

Question

1 How can you help someone who is going through a bereavement? (See pages 148 and 155–57 for further ideas.)

losing someone you have loved and it causes a major change in people's lives. There is a very strong sense of loss – you might lose the main person you talked to, the main person who helped you, your sexual partner, a person with whom you shared your life and a person who made you feel good. Living without a partner can involve great uncertainty. Your partner may have helped with household bills or with shopping or housework – now you have to do it all yourself. Bereavement can mean you have to learn to live a new life as a single person again. Learning to cope on your own can take a lot of time and energy.

People who try to cope with a major loss often experience feelings of:

⋄   disbelief the person is dead

⋄   sadness and depression

⋄   anger or guilt

⋄   stress because they have to learn to cope with a different lifestyle.

Few people describe bereavement as a positive life event, but the final outcome need not only be sadness and grief. Over time, people can take a positive outlook on life again. Read the case study on page 145. Nathan has come through the experience in a positive way even though he will always wish his partner had never died. Bereavement can lead people to start what might feel like 'a new life'. Bereavement need not be understood as totally negative.

Physical changes

As we grow older our bodies change and this change may alter the way we think about ourselves, our self-image and self-concept. Some changes like puberty are expected. Some research suggests that boys who start puberty early tend to gain increased self-esteem, while boys who go through the changes late tend to have lower self-esteem. Girls who start puberty either well before or well after other girls in their class seem to have lower self-esteem throughout their adolescence.

Other changes, such as injury and illness, can be unexpected and very negative in their effects. A sudden disability, such as the loss of sight or the loss of a limb, can cause a person to react in a similar way to the loss of a friend or relative. As well as a major sense of loss and uncertainty about the future, injury can cause problems with self-esteem and self-image. Older people who lose limbs will often say such things as: 'I'm not going to the doctor – other people will look at me. I don't want to go out, I'm worried that other people will talk about me.' Learning to cope with major physical change can be very difficult for some people.

Types of support

Coping with change is easier if you have other people to help you. Most people have family and friends to help them cope with change. Family and friends can provide help and support to meet different types of needs.

Physical needs

Friends and family can often provide practical help to help meet people's physical needs. For example, moving house or grief can make a person feel very tired. Friends and family might do practical things, such as helping with housework or shopping. Practical help can take the pressure off a person who feels tired. Examples of practical help include:

⋄   helping move furniture when a person moves house

⋄   giving money when a person gets married

⋄   baby-sitting when a person is going through a divorce

⋄   providing transport for a person who is physically disabled.

Intellectual needs

Family and friends can help people to understand change. Sometimes they may be able to offer useful advice or information to help with change if they have coped with similar problems before. Examples of advice and information include:

⋄   advice about managing money when a person moves house

⋄   information about support and adaptations available for a person with a disability

⋄   sharing own experiences of loss or grief.

Emotional needs

Family and friends often give us an emotional 'safe place' to get away from stress and pressure. Friends and family help us to feel valued – to feel we are important. Our sense of self-esteem usually develops out of our relationship with family or carers. Friends can support us through periods of stressful change by helping us to feel we matter.

Examples of emotional support include:

- listening to one another
- using conversation to show that we understand how other people feel
- making other people feel important or valued.

Social needs

Friends and family create groups of people we belong to. Mixing with other people who like us is very important when we have to cope with changes in our life. Friends and family influence our self-concept. Change is easier if we can talk to and be with other people. Examples of social support include:

- visiting relatives in hospital
- being able to talk to parents about marriage or divorce
- talking to friends about new jobs or moving house.

Professional carers

Paid and voluntary care workers can provide many of the types of support friends and family give. Some people do not have friends and family and need professional support. Professional carers may also provide more specialised services. Professional care includes the following:

- Doctors (GPs) who can offer advice and drugs to help with stress.
- Counsellors who can offer skilled listening and emotional support.
- Voluntary services, such as *Relate* which provides counselling about relationships and marriage, *Victim Support* which provides advice and emotional support for victims of crime and *Cruise* which provides support for people who are bereaved.
- Citizens' Advice Bureau which can offer advice on a whole range of issues, including equipment to help people with disabilities.
- Social care services, such as residential care, day care and home care which provides social, emotional and practical care.
- Early years services, such as playgroups and nurseries, which provide for intellectual development as well as other needs.

As well as providing specialised support, professional carers also help people to cope with change by:

- using their understanding of people and change
- using good listening and communication skills (see Unit 1 for details)
- working with values that respect the diversity, rights and confidentiality of clients (see Unit 1 for details).

Support for individuals experiencing life changes

Expected change

Starting a new school

A child's family can help by understanding what is involved. Most children feel a little afraid at leaving their parents and being with different people. Going to school involves learning to be more independent. A family might help their child by the following means:

- Providing playgroup experiences before the child starts school, so that the child is used to meeting others and change is less sudden.
- Praising their child for his or her independent behaviour.
- Talking to the child before going to school and afterwards.
- Showing love and affection – being away from parents does not mean you have lost them.

Professional carers, teachers and classroom assistants might help by understanding the change children face. Carers can help by:

- being careful to include all children in social activities
- providing a warm, friendly, emotionally safe atmosphere for children
- learning about individual children's needs – listening to children
- praising children's achievement.

Starting a new job

Friends and family can help by listening and talking. Talking helps people to understand their own emotions and thoughts. There is a saying: 'I know what I think, when I hear what I say.' Starting a new job involves worries about doing well and being accepted. Talking and listening will help to meet a person's emotional needs. Sometimes friends and family may also be able to give helpful advice or practical help with getting to work and so on.

Change is often stressful and stress is tiring. Friends and family may help by understanding this. Colleagues at work can help by listening to and understanding the needs of a new worker. They can help with advice. They can also help by creating a welcoming social atmosphere that will help the new worker to feel included in a new group of people.

Marriage

Marriage can imply a new lifestyle, moving home, developing a deep attachment to a partner and preparing to look after children.

Friends can family can help by:

- listening and talking to help people cope with the emotional need to change
- offering advice
- giving practical help with organising the marriage ceremony and so on
- creating a warm, friendly, social environment where new relatives and relationships are accepted.

Professionals can help by offering counselling and spiritual advice. Most religions will offer some emotional and spiritual support.

Unexpected change

Death of a friend or relative

Friends and relatives can help in the following ways:

- *Listening and talking*: there is an old saying 'A problem shared is a problem halved'. The loss of a person you loved can leave you with the problem of making sense of your life. Being able to talk about it can help.
- *Doing practical work*: grief can make you tired – if other people do shopping or housework this can help you to cope.
- *Providing company*: many people who are grieving need to have other people around them.

Professionals can help in the following ways:

- Listening, talking and showing they respect and value the person.
- Doing practical work: home-care services might help with housework.
- Providing social support and company: self-help groups and day and residential services can meet social needs.
- Specialist help (counselling): some people need expert help in making sense of and adjusting to their loss. Professional counselling can help people to cope with change.
- Specialist help (advice): sometimes the loss of a relative might leave people with practical worries about expenses, loss of benefits, legal issues and so on. Organisations such as the Citizens' Advice Bureau or a social worker may be able to offer help with these worries.

Divorce

The emotions people go through when relationships break up are often not very different from the feelings people have when they lose someone through death. In many ways the help people need will be similar to the help needed in bereavement. People will still need to talk and be listened to. People will still benefit from practical help. People will still want company and may benefit from advice. Sometimes divorce creates special problems to do with looking after children or financial problems. Specialist legal help may be needed in this situation. Some people may have strong feelings of anger, guilt or depression. Counselling may be an important service for these people.

Redundancy

Some people may welcome the chance to change their job, but others may experience emotions similar to those who lose someone they loved. People who have been made redundant from a job they liked may need to talk through their feelings. Practical help and advice may be useful. Some people may need professional counselling or help from employment agencies to help them to cope with the changes they face.

Physical injury or loss of health

Damage to sight or hearing, or a sudden loss of health or mobility, can cause a major change to the way a person sees him or herself. People who experience physical loss will often feel the need for:

- company

- conversation and listening

- practical help

- advice and help with learning to cope with a changed life.

In some ways a loss of health or ability can be similar to the loss of a loved relative in terms of the help needed.

Think it over

If one of your group had a sports accident and was told he or she will never walk again, what support could you give him or her?

What support might the person need from professionals?

Unit 3 Assessment

Unlike Units 1 and 2, this unit is tested externally. To help you with this, this section provides further analysis of the issues involved in personal development. Its focus is on those things you must be able to do to assist you in gaining a merit or distinction grade.

Revision for test

You will be expected to read short case studies and answer questions on:

- the physical characteristics of different life stages

- the social and economic factors that affect development

- the social and economic factors that influence self-concept

- the support individuals may expect when they experience life changes.

Analysing the positive and negative effects of personal relationships on an individual's development and self-concept

Most real people do not have such a happy and positive story to tell about the development of self-concept. Things might go wrong for many people.

CASE STUDY – Anil

Anil is male and was born in 1982. When Anil was young he lived in a large household with his mother and father, older sister and grandmother. Anil received constant attention from these family members and was never left on his own. All the family loved him and had time to play with him. Anil soon learned to recognise his family and he made a close emotional bond with them. Anil's first two years of life provided him with a feeling of being safe and of belonging to the family.

In early childhood Anil was encouraged to play with other children in neighbouring houses. Anil learned to mix and play with others and began to imagine the things they did. Anil felt he mattered and that he was liked by his parents and friends. Anil's parents brought him up to be polite and to behave appropriately. They encouraged Anil to learn to read and write, and play computer games. The family could afford to buy books, a

computer and a TV for Anil. At school, Anil made friends with many other children and usually received praise from his teachers. By the age of 9 years, Anil felt he was good at school and asked if he could do homework like his older sister.

At around 10 years of age Anil began to take an interest in his appearance: he began to be concerned that he had stylish clothes – not old clothes like some of the younger children. Anil also took an interest in his hairstyle.

Anil began to compare himself with other children. Anil decided that he was not the fastest or the cleverest boy in his class, but he was good at football and he was good at maths and most other school work.

By the age of 11 years, Anil had a general sense of self-confidence and a deep feeling of belonging to his family and friendship groups. Anil also felt that he 'looked OK'. Anil had a range of positive feelings about himself. These feelings were due to his earlier life experience.

Anil started secondary school and made new friends there. His school work was often praised and his parents said they were proud of him. Anil sometimes won sports competitions and other boys often asked his advice or wanted to be with him. Anil continued to develop a positive sense of self-esteem and self-worth during secondary school.

Around the age of 15 years, Anil became very concerned about being seen as attractive by the girls he mixed with. By 16 years, Anil decided he was popular and attractive. Anil worked hard for his exams; he did this mainly because his parents

brought him up – or socialised him – to value hard work and educational success.

Anil made friends with a couple of other boys who were very interested in the media and computers. Anil decided to study media and computing, with the idea of making a career in this area.

Now that Anil is older he has set up his own business with one of his old friends and with financial help from his family. Anil has a close, loving relationship with his girlfriend and they plan to marry next year. Anil is a very confident adult; he feels he is good at what he does for a living. He has a very positive self-concept, he feels he is important to his local community, valued by his family, loved by his girlfriend and highly respected by the people he works with.

For a Merit grade you need to be able to analyse the positive and negative effects of relationships on an individual's development and self-concept. Looking at Anil's story above, can you analyse how relationships have had a positive effect on him? You need to think about the following:

- Early relationships and attachments in infancy.

- Early childhood relationships with parents and family, and the degree of safety and security he felt at home.

- Friendships with other children – what values and ways of behaving did he learn?

- Relationships with teachers and other adults – how did this influence his self-concept?

- Relationships with friends and partners during adolescence and early adulthood.

- Friendship networks across life.

You might look for the positive steps in the development of a person's self-concept, as shown in Figure 3.42.

You could use these steps to help you analyse other case studies. The question to ask is: 'Did relationships help the person to achieve a positive self-concept, or did relationships have a negative effect by blocking the development of a positive self-concept?'

Analysing the positive and negative effects of personal relationships on Anil's self-concept

The diagram in Figure 3.43 analyses the many positive influences on Anil's developing self-concept. Even in Anil's story, some issues could be seen as negative (two are noted in the figure). At Distinction level you have to consider which factor has had the most significant influence on the development and self-concept of one person in a case study. To do this you have to make up an argument that one issue is particularly

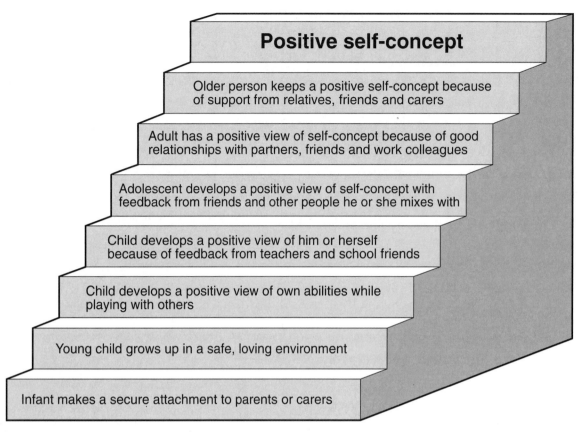

Figure 3.42   The positive steps in the development of self-concept

important in influencing development and self-concept. This is hard to do because, in real life, all the different influences combine together to influence our development. At Distinction level you have to choose an influence and make an argument that this particular influence can be seen as more important than the others.

When trying to analyse a case study it is important to ask the right questions. You might like to use the diagram in Figure 3.44 to help you think about case studies you work with. Looking back at Anil's case study, we can see the following:

Relationships had an influence: Anil made an attachment to his parents, he was influenced by the norms and values of his family.

Economic factors had an influence: his parents brought him books, a computer and

TV to help him with his learning.

Appearance had an influence: Anil had a positive self-image because he thought many other people found him attractive.

Local environment might have had an influence: Anil mixed with people who valued education and learning.

Culture had an influence: the story does not give details, but Anil was influenced by his family's values and these may have been influenced by class values, and by values associated with religious and ethnic traditions.

Gender role is involved in the story: Anil and his male friends were especially interested in computers. Boys may see computers as a very appropriate thing for men to work with – male gender-role expectations might be involved with this.

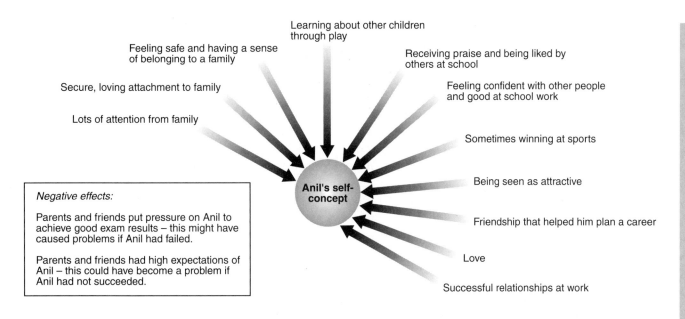

Figure 3.43   The positive and negative effects of personal relationships on Anil's self-concept

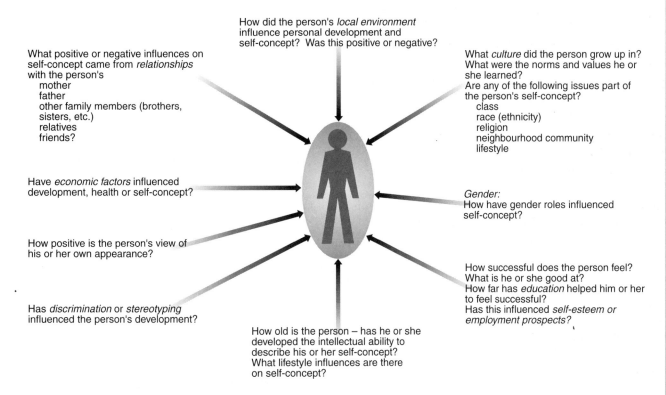

Figure 3.44   Questions to ask about development when analysing a case study

Anil also felt proud of being good at football – perhaps because he was fulfilling expectations of male sporting roles.

Education had an influence: Anil did well at school and started to expect he would do well in his career. His success at school influenced his self-esteem and his future employment prospects.

Which influence was most significant?

Go through the list and decide how strong a case you could make for each factor. Discuss the possibilities with friends. There may not be much you can write about some influences – you could choose to leave these. A particular influence might seem interesting – and this might be the best area to choose. For instance, appearance only started to matter at the age of 15 years – perhaps it was only a small part of what made Anil confident and successful. Anil's parents bought him a computer – but perhaps this was only a small help in developing his self-confidence. The story does not tell us much about local environment or culture, so perhaps it is best not to pick these areas. Gender role is interesting, but it is difficult to explain how Anil's whole concept of self and self-worth is influenced by gender. Perhaps relationships or educational influences might be the best influences to write about.

What could be written about relationships?

Anil had positive relationships throughout his life. He made a secure attachment to his parents which laid the foundation for a happy and positive life. Early relationships may be particularly important, because they are the first relationships we make and they may influence all our later relationships. Looking back to the steps to developing a positive sense of self (Figure 3.42), we could write about the way relationships helped Anil to develop feelings of self-worth, confidence and a very positive self-concept. Looking back at the diagram of the effects of relationships on Anil (Figure 3.43), you can see a wide range of influences.

Using all these ideas you can make an argument that relationships had the most significant influence on Anil's development and self-concept. You could argue that, if he

had not had all these positive relationships, he would be a very different person – probably less confident, unsuccessful, with low self-esteem and much less happiness and success in life.

What could be written about education?

Anil grew up in a family that valued learning and that expected Anil to work hard and to do well. Anil's parents bought books and computers to help him. Anil mixed with friends and lived in a culture that encouraged him to learn and to do well at school. Looking back to the section on education earlier in this unit, Figure 3.43 shows how positive expectations can lead to success – this diagram could be used to explain how Anil developed a very positive view of his own abilities. It could be argued that Anil's success at school and at work were caused by family and social expectations of him, and the development of a self-concept which included being confident and successful. Anil's success at school could be argued to be the most significant influence on his development and self-concept. You could argue that, if Anil had not had these expectations and experiences, then he may have developed a sense of being a failure and have grown up to be much less confident, with lower self-esteem and much less happiness and success in life.

When writing about real people you can only guess which factor has had the most significant influence on their development. A Distinction grade is not given for being right, but for the quality of thinking that goes into your answer.

Relevant support

You need to understand case studies that describe people who need support. You need to be able to pick out the major changes that have happened in someone's life and describe what kind of help and support might help a person to cope with expected changes, such as starting school, starting a new job, leaving home, marriage and retirement.

Using a case study, such as Rahim's or Anil's story (pages 141 and 150), pick out key changes and then use the headings Physical, Intellectual, Emotional and Social to describe the help friends, family and professionals might give people to help them cope with change.

For a *Merit* grade you need to cover unexpected change as well as the expected events covered for a *Pass*. This means you should explain some of the emotions that might come with such losses as bereavement, divorce, redundancy, loss of health or ability. You need to explain how talking and listening can help people to cope with change. You should give examples of practical help and advice, and explain how these forms of help are useful.

At *Distinction* level you need to explore different ways people react to change and how these different reactions could affect the type of help and support needed. You might use the following section on reaction to change to help you compare and contrast different case studies that describe people who are coping with change.

Different reactions to change
Most people spend time thinking about their future and wishing for good things to happen. Children often want to start school; adolescents and adults might want to start work. Some people want to get married. Some people even welcome redundancy because they want to stop work. If change is seen as positive, then people do not have the same emotional problems as when change is seen as negative.

If people feel they have lost something, or if people feel they are not the same person any more, then they are likely to see change as negative. When people see change as

negative they try to avoid making a change. Emotionally, people want to 'run away' or 'fight' the need to change.

Coping with negative change and loss (*Distinction* level theory)

A famous author called John Bowlby researched child development during the 1940s. He believed that most people would form close emotional attachments during their lives. When an attachment is broken, the first reaction is the pain of separation and a desperate desire to find the lost person again. When a partner (or close family member) dies, the first phase of grief may focus on the desire, somehow, to find the dead person again. During this first phase, the individual is unable to change. He or she has to let go of his or her past expectations that are focused on the lost person before change is possible. Because the person is denying the fact of death, this phase is called **denial**.

In the second phase of grief, the bereaved person may experience strong feelings, such as guilt, anger or despair. This phase involves developing a degree of detachment from the dead person.

In the third and final phase, the grieving person reorganises his or her sense of self, expectations and habits. This is the stage when an individual starts to rebuild his or her life. This rebuilding or reconstruction is, perhaps, like reconstructing a tower of cards after it has fallen down (see Figure 3.45).

In summary, grief may often involve three phases:

- denial and searching for the lost person
- feelings of despair, anger and guilt
- rebuilding a new life.

Going through a bereavement involves coping with a massive amount of unwelcome change. An expert on grief, Colin Murray Parkes, explained that going through a change involves a need for

The development of a sense of self takes time and effort

A sudden change can threaten an individual's self-concept

Reconstruction takes time

Figure 3.45   The construction of identity may be like building a tower of cards

psychological work and this takes time and effort. Much of the pain and sorrow associated with loss may be connected with people's reaction to resist change. Parkes wrote: 'Resistance to change, the reluctance to give up possessions, people, status, expectations – this I believe, is the basis of

grief.' *Bereavement*, C. Murray Parkes (Penguin, 1995).

Parkes described the process of grieving. Each person experiences the struggle of grief differently, but there may be some general components of coping with change that might be identified. Some reactions are listed below.

Denial

If a person is told a relative is dead, or that he or she will be made redundant, or has a serious illness, that person may react with denial. Denial means the person may refuse to believe the information, saying such things as:

- 'No, it's not him that's dead – you must have the wrong name.'
- 'No, this is a bad joke, I've always worked here.'
- 'I can't have diabetes, no one else in my family has it.'

Sometimes people will deny the importance of what they have been told:

- 'Oh, it's terrible that he died, but I'm all right, I can cope. It doesn't make any difference to my life.'
- 'Oh, they're getting rid of me soon, but I'm all right, it doesn't matter.'
- 'Oh, lot's of people have my illness – it won't really affect me.'

People often deny the seriousness of a problem when they are stressed and in a state of shock. At this stage it may be very important not to challenge people or argue with them about their feelings. Very often the most helpful support is to offer to:

- provide practical help with day-to-day tasks
- provide company
- listen if the person wants to talk.   .

Professional counselling may help some people to cope without needing to deny a loss or the seriousness of that loss.

Anger or guilt

Coming to terms with loss is a difficult process and some people will try to cope by wanting to blame others or blame themselves. Blaming and being angry with others can sometimes help a grieving person to make sense of what has happened. Blaming others may also help some people to avoid experiencing the full pain of their loss. Guilt can be a similar emotion. By blaming yourself it helps to make sense of things. It may also help some people to change their view of themselves and slowly recover from a loss. Although anger and guilt can help people to adjust, they can also be very unpleasant emotions.

Ways of helping people who feel angry or guilty include the following:

- Listening may help them understand their feelings. It is possible to listen and be good company without agreeing with everything a person says, or arguing with a person.

- Practical help can be very important if they feel stressed and tired because of their emotions.

- It is usually important not to agree with statements about blame, or argue with people who feel anger or guilt.

Professional counselling may help some people who find it hard to cope with their emotions. People who are seriously stressed may be helped by their doctor, who may be able to prescribe drugs or refer the person for counselling or other specialist help.

Withdrawal

Sometimes people 'give up' when very serious things go wrong. Some grieving people refuse company, become depressed and sometimes stop looking after themselves. People who seriously neglect themselves might benefit from an assessment of their mental health or care needs. Care staff may try to build an relationship and to provide practical help to people who are depressed or withdrawn. It may sometimes be appropriate to encourage a person who is withdrawn to see his or her doctor.

Sometimes people experience a feeling of **depersonalisation**. Depersonalisation is the feeling you are not really there, that you are watching yourself from outside. Things that happen seem unreal.

As with other reactions, listening and showing respect and value are key care skills. Practical support and providing company – to meet social needs – are also important.

Trying out or testing ways of coping

As people begin to come to terms with loss, they may experiment with new behaviours, ideas or lifestyles. Very often a person may want to talk about new activities or places they could go to. Some people may ask your advice about clubs or interests they could take up, or just want to talk through their memories of their past life as they come to accept their life has changed. Talking and listening may help people to imagine a new or different life. Care of some older people involves **reminiscence work** where people are encouraged to remember and talk about their past. Reminiscence activities may help some people to test ideas for coping.

Unit 3 Test

Scenario one

Anil is 2 years old and lives with his mother and father, his older sister and grandmother in a large semi-detached house. Anil's mother goes to work, but while she is at work his grandmother looks after him. Anil is well looked after and has developed as expected for a 2-year-old.

1   Think of one way in which children develop in each of the following areas during the first two years of life:

   - physically
   - intellectually
   - emotionally
   - socially.

2   Put the following stages of physical development into the order in which they generally occur:

   - toilet training
   - sitting
   - crawling
   - walking alone
   - bear-walking.

3   Explain ways in which Anil's family might help him to develop his intellectual abilities.

4   Anil always has a member of his family with him. Explain one way in which this might be positive for Anil's emotional development.

5   Anil's sister is 5 years old. Think of one way in which she will be more developed than Anil intellectually.

6   Anil's mother and father both work in order to have enough money to run the home; they often look tired and complain they do not have enough time to do the things they want. If Anil's parents become very stressed because of this, how might this stress affect Anil?

7   Anil's grandmother is 70 years old. Think of three physical changes that are common in old age.

8   Anil's grandmother chooses to live with the rest of the family. How might living with the rest of the family influence her self-concept?

9   Anil's grandmother spends a lot of time praising him and his sister. She is very interested in helping them to develop. How will praise and interest be likely to affect the development of the children's self-concept?

10   Anil's grandmother grew up at a time when it was assumed that women would usually look after the home and children while men went to work. What is the difference between men and women's social role usually called?

11   Name three things which will be important to help Anil develop a positive self-concept by the time he is 18 years of age.

12   Which issues listed below will be cultural influences on Anil's self-concept?

   - going with his family to worship at the local temple
   - mixing with other children at school
   - eating a balanced diet
   - taking regular exercise.

Scenario two

Tola is 16 years old and she lives with her mother in a flat on a low-income housing estate. Tola has many friends at school but she is looking forward to leaving and getting a job. Tola's ambition is to move into a flat with her boyfriend once they have enough money.

13   Tola's household does not have much money. Name four different types of stress that may be more common in

low-income households than in better-off households.

14 Tola's mother is going through the menopause. Which of the following is responsible for the menopause?

- her children are grown up and have left home
- there are no eggs left in the woman's ovaries
- she has stopped having sexual intercourse
- she has reached the age of 45 years.

15 Tola passed through the life stage of puberty a few years ago. Name two physical changes she will have experienced at this time.

16 If Tola succeeds in getting a well paid job, how will this affect her self-concept?

17 If Tola moves out of the flat she shares with her mother, name two examples of change Tola may be likely to experience in relation to her self-concept.

18 Tola's mother cares for Tola's grandmother, who lives two miles away. Tola's grandmother recently slipped and fell over at home. Why might older people be more at risk of accidents than younger adults?

19 Think of one example of each type of need Tola will have if she starts a new job:

- physical
- intellectual
- emotional
- social.

20 Tola's mother may miss her after she has moved out. She may feel a sense of loss, or even grief. Name three emotional reactions people often experience when they have to adjust to change.

UNIT 3 ASSESSMENT

Access Means by which an individual becomes a client of a particular service.

Acute A condition which starts quickly and lasts for a short time, such as a common cold.

Adrenaline Hormone released when the body is anticipating any form of stress.

Advocate Someone who speaks on behalf of another person.

Aerobic Needing air or oxygen.

Aerobic respiration Cell respiration in the presence of plenty of oxygen.

AIDS Acquired immune deficiency syndrome, a collection of disorders that result in time from HIV infection.

Anaerobic Without air or oxygen.

Appearance How we look. People use different clothes, hairstyles, cosmetics and adornments such as jewellery to express membership of particular age groups, class groups, cultural and friendship groups.

Babbling A stage infants go through before they can use language. The infant makes sounds which may later help him or her to use words.

Baby talk Adults use a high-pitched voice and slow down their speech when talking to infants. Adults may also use exaggerated facial expressions. Baby talk may help to keep an infant's attention.

Balanced diet A diet that has carbohydrates, fats and proteins in the correct proportions and enough vitamins and mineral salts, fibre and water to ensure healthy living.

Balanced lifestyle Having enough rest, leisure, exercise, work and an appropriate diet to maintain health. Not having too much leisure or work, or inappropriate eating habits.

BASW British Association of Social Work.

Belonging A feeling of identifying with a particular group of people. Feeling safe and supported by a particular group.

Bereavement The loss of a person that you loved. Bereavement often involves strong emotions of disbelief, denial, anger, guilt and resisting change.

BMI Body Mass Index – a person's weight in kilograms divided by his or her height in metres.

Bonding Making an emotional attachment to a person. Babies usually make an attachment to carers during their first year of life.

Buffering Partners, friends and family may protect a person from the full stress of life changes and conflicts. Michael Argyle called this protection buffering.

Career routes The pathway which an individual takes in order to qualify and then move to more senior roles in a certain job or profession.

Care Value Base Principles that guide how care workers should behave. Key principles include valuing diversity, promoting rights and responsibilities and maintaining confidentiality.

Carer Anyone who provides care for another person or people.

Change Life involves coping with a wide variety of change – some of which is welcome and some of which is not. Change can be classified as predictable or unpredictable.

Charters Documents which set up or explain the rights that people may expect.

Child Support Agency A government agency that deals with setting the level of maintenance money that absent parents are required to pay towards the keep of their children.

Class A group of people who share a common position in society. Class membership is linked to occupation, income, wealth, beliefs and lifestyle.

Client Anyone who receives a service – a general term which covers patient, service user and customer.

Code of practice A set of principles which can be used to guide and measure the quality of care practice.

Cognition A term which covers the mental processes involved in understanding and knowing.

Cognitive development The development of thinking and reasoning ability. Cognitive includes the study of perception, language and learning performance.

Commissioning The process of determining and securing health and social care services.

Communication cycle The process of building an understanding of what another person is communicating.

Community Care Charter Documents which explain what people may expect from community care services within a geographical area.

Community health care Care provided for individuals in the community and, where possible, in their own homes.

Complementary therapies Therapies such as aromatherapy, reflexology and acupuncture that have not traditionally been available through the National Health Service.

Concrete operations The third stage of intellectual development in Jean Piaget's theory. At this stage, individuals can solve logical problems provided they can see or sense the objects with which they are working. At this stage, people cannot cope with abstract problems.

Contracting The process for agreeing the nature, level and standard of service that is to be provided.

Contracts Formal legal agreements to ensure the delivery of services.

Controlled drugs Illegal drugs.

Control of Substances Hazardous to Health (COSHH) Regulations, 1988 Requirements to be met by all people who deal with dangerous substances at work.

Cultural differences Differences due to different life and learning experiences which can affect communication and understanding.

Culture The collection of values and norms associated with a group. Culture is intended to describe all the features of a group that make it different and distinct from other groups.

Dementia A term which covers a range of illnesses involving the degeneration (or wasting) of the brain. Dementia is not part of normal ageing. Most very old people show no sign of dementing illness.

Denial Saying or believing something is not true. Denial is also a defence or stage in reacting to change. People often block unwanted changes and deny that they are real. People may deny that someone has died or deny that the consequences of the death will matter.

Department of Health (DOH) A central government body which administers health and social care.

Department of Social Security (DSS) Government department responsible for the provision of welfare benefits.

Development When a person or system alters how he, she or it functions.

Developmental maturity The degree to which a person or an ability is 'mature' or 'adult like'.

Dialect Different sounds and words which can result in communication differences.

Differential growth rates While general bodily growth occurs fairly steadily throughout childhood, the nervous system grows rapidly in the first few years of life and the reproductive organs hardly grow until puberty.

Dignity Being respected by others, not being controlled or abused.

Direct care Care that is given on a face-to-face basis.

Discrimination Giving a better (or worse) quality of service to some people than to others because of their gender, ethnicity, sexuality, age, social class or other group membership.

Diversity The way in which people are different from one another. Key differences include race, gender, religion, age, class and sexual orientation.

DOH *see* **Department of Health**

DSS *see* **Department of Social Security**

Duty Services that an organisation is required by legislature to provide.

Emotional development How we learn to develop self-esteem, self-concept and understand and respond to emotion.

Emotional health How people deal with and express emotions such as fear, grief, happiness etc.

Empowerment Giving power to others – enabling others to take control of their lives and make their own choices. The opposite of controlling other people.

Energy Stored work.

Environmental barriers Environmental barriers include noise and poor lighting, both of which can block communication.

Ethnicity A word used for 'race'. Some people used to think that biological differences created different races. Nowadays, social scientists use the term ethnicity to make it clear that we are talking about social classification and not physical differences.

Extended family A family which consists of parents and their children, and other relatives such as grandparents, uncles or aunts.

Fieldwork A term used in social care that refers to the work of professionals, usually social workers, who work in the community.

Fine motor skills Control over small, careful movements, such as when cutting out shapes or picking up tiny objects.

Formal operations The fourth and final stage in Piaget's theory of intellectual development. People with formal logical operations can solve abstract problems.

Gestures Hand and arm movements that can send messages about how we feel.

GP fundholders General practitioners who hold budgets with which they can buy health care for their patients.

Gross motor skills Control over large movements, such as when running or jumping.

Growth When the body or an organ of the body gets bigger.

HA *see* **Health Authorities**

Health And Safety At Work Act (HASAW) 1974 Deals with the health and safety of people at work.

Health Authorities (HA) Regional departments within the NHS which have responsibility for commissioning and purchasing health care within their area.

Healthy lifestyle Daily activities and routines which promote physical and mental health and well-being such as a balanced diet, enough exercise, enough rest, work and leisure. The term usually includes an avoidance of unhealthy habits such as smoking and substance abuse.

HIV Human immuno-deficiency virus that infects people who exchange body fluids with infected persons.

Holistic Treating a person as a whole individual by looking at all relevant issues and not just the details of certain symptoms.

Home life A code of practice for residential care.

Homelessness Not having a home in which to live.

Income Money received as wages, interest on savings or profits from business activities.

Independence Being able to function without being dependent on others. Adolescence is seen as a time of growing independence in Western culture.

Indirect care Services provided to support direct care, e.g. the ambulance service.

Informal care Care given by people who are not paid for the care they give, e.g. family or friends.

Intellectual development The development of our ability to think, reason and understand. Here, the term covers use of language, remembering, thinking and the development of knowledge.

Intellectual health How people think and organise their thinking.

Jargon Technical talk which is hard to understand.

Kilojoules SI units that measure energy. They have replaced calories and kilocalories (Calories).

Life chances The opportunities which are really open to individuals. People are born into different social class and wealth categories. These categories may restrict or enhance the opportunities that people have to be healthy or wealthy.

Life changes Major changes in life include starting school, starting a new job, leaving home, marriage, retirement. These changes usually alter a person's self-concept.

Life stages Infancy, childhood, puberty and adolescence, adulthood and old age. Life stages are ways of looking at people's life-span and breaking it into sections.

Lifestyle choice A choice made by individuals about the way in which they lead their lives.

Listening Trying to understand the messages that other people send us. Listening is an active process which involves more than simply hearing what is said.

Local Authority Social Services Departments which provide social care to meet the needs of people in the community.

Lone-parent families A family consisting of one parent and children.

Maternal deprivation John Bowlby's theory that children would become emotionally damaged if separated from their mother during a critical period of their early life.

Means testing This is when an individual's income and savings are taken into account when deciding on the cost of a service to a client, or whether he or she is eligible to receive the service.

Mixed economy of care Care provided by a mixture of statutory agencies, voluntary and private organisations and informal care givers.

Muscle tension Our muscles – particularly the muscles in the hands and face – can send messages about how we feel.

Menopause Cessation of menstruation, usually occurring naturally between the ages of 45 and 55.

Moral development People's views on what is right or wrong are influenced by their cognitive development and how they have learned to think. Adults usually have more complex ways of understanding right and wrong than do children.

Motor development How muscles co-ordinate and pull together to enable more and more complicated movements to occur.

Multi-disciplinary team A team consisting of people from different professions e.g. doctors, nurses, occupational therapists and social workers.

National Health Service (NHS) In England the Secretary of State for Health has overall responsibility for the NHS.

National Health Service and Community Care Act 1990 An Act of Parliament which aims to allow more vulnerable people to live as independently as possible, within their own homes or in a homely setting in the community.

National Society for the Prevention of Cruelty to Children (NSPCC) Charity founded in 1889 to act in the interests of children's safety.

Neonate A new-born baby.

NHS *see* **National Health Service**

NHS trust A free-standing body within the NHS that has responsibility for determining its own structure and spending.

Norms The rules of behaviour which are followed by members of groups. Norms are what is expected as being 'normal' things to do.

NSPCC *see* **National Society for the Prevention of Cruelty to Children**

Nuclear family A family consisting of parents and their children who share a residence and co-operate economically and socially.

Oestrogen A female sex hormone (actually a group of hormones) responsible for secondary sexual characteristics.

Opportunistic infections Infections that occur when immunity is low, as in HIV and AIDS cases; normally the immune system would prevent opportunistic infections from happening.

Over-the-counter drugs Drugs such as cough medicine and aspirin that do not require a prescription; they can be bought in any chemist or pharmacy shop.

Passive smoking Inhaling unfiltered smoke from other people's tobacco materials.

Patient's Charter A document which sets out the rights and standards people can expect from the NHS. A new charter will probably be mainly concerned with standards of service rather than rights as such.

PCG *see* **Primary Care Group**

Peak flow The maximum speed at which air can be forced out of the lungs.

Physical health Health related to the functioning of the human body.

PIES This stands for physical, intellectual, emotional and social. It is a way of understanding the different aspects of human development.

Play Play enables children to learn by exploring, to practise skills, to learn to use imagination in order to understand how things work and to understand social roles. Play also helps people to meet emotional needs and adult 'recreation' often involves 'play'.

Posture The way we sit or stand sends messages about how we feel.

Poverty Not having enough wealth or income to be able to live like the majority of people in this country.

Pre-operational The second stage in Jean Piaget's theory of intellectual development. Pre-operational children are understood as being pre-logical. They cannot reason logically.

Prescribed drugs Drugs that require a prescription from a doctor.

Primary Care Group (PCG) In England, a PCG is comprised of GPs and community nurses, covering a population of approximately 1000,000, and having responsibility for commissioning primary and secondary health care.

Primary care Health care provided in the community, e.g. GP services and dentistry.

Private organisations / services Services offered by businesses which are intending to make a profit.

Prognosis A prediction of the probable course and outcome of a disease.

Provider An organisation that sells its services to a purchaser.

Puberty The period of change leading towards being capable of sexual reproduction.

Public health services A branch of the NHS that deals mainly with the prevention of ill health.

Purchaser An organisation that buys in necessary care.

Reconstituted families A family which is made up of children from previous family groups. The couple are not both the parents of each child in the family.

Referral Methods by which a client is referred or passed to a service.

Secondary care Health care that is often curative in nature and is given in hospitals, clinics and surgeries.

Seebohm Report Government report published in 1968 which resulted in the amalgamation of the children's and welfare departments within local authorities.

Self-concept The way we use concepts to understand who we are. A clear understanding of self may be necessary for independent functioning in Western society.

Self-confidence An individual's confidence in his or her ability to achieve something or cope with a situation. Self-confidence may influence and be influenced by self-esteem.

Self-esteem How much a person values him or herself and his or her life. High self-esteem may help a person to feel happy and confident. Low self-esteem may lead to depression and unhappiness.

Self-help groups Groups which meet to help individuals with particular concerns.

Self-image The way we imagine and visualise ourselves – similar to self-concept.

Self-worth The value or esteem we place on ourselves. A sense of worth is a more general feature of development which may exist before adolescent and adult self-esteem needs develop.

Sensorimotor The first stage in Jean Piaget's theory of intellectual development. Infants learn to co-ordinate their muscle movements in relation to what they think makes sense.

Services Help which is provided to support individual and community needs.

Sexual maturity A stage of physical development that results in the ability of males and females to reproduce.

Slang Informal terms which some people may not understand.

Social context A setting where social influences affect an individual's learning and development.

Social development How people make relationships and interact with others. Learning to relate to family, friends and wider society.

Social exclusion People who are excluded from opportunities to have a healthy and economically comfortable life. Some factors which create social exclusion are poverty, discrimination and stressful living conditions.

Social health How people form relationships with other people.

Social inclusion Including people in opportunities to lead a healthy and economically active life.

Socialisation The process of learning the norms and values of a group, and developing a role within it. Through socialisation people become part of a group or culture.

Socioeconomic The interaction of social (relating to the society in which a person lives) and economic (to do with money) factors.

Status A measure of the rank and prestige of a person. Status helps to explain how people see themselves.

Statutory services Services set up because of a legal requirement to provide a service.

Stereotyping Seeing members of a group as all being the same.

Stress management Finding ways to reduce stress or cope with it.

Sub-culture Group values and beliefs which are shared by a particular set of people, but which differ in some way from general values and beliefs within a recognisable culture.

Tertiary care Health care often provided in specialist units, or units that are rehabilitative in nature.

Threat Something which is understood as a danger to physical, social or emotional well-being.

UKCC The United Kingdom Central Council for Nursing, Midwifery and Health Visiting.

Unified structure The combining of health and social care at an organisational level, e.g. the Northern Ireland department of health and social care.

Value base The values which guide professional behaviour in health and care work. Current NVQ standards identify valuing diversity, promoting rights and responsibility and confidentiality as key values.

Vegans People who eat or use no animal products at all.

Vegetarian people who eat no slaughtered (killed) meat or fish but who will eat milk, eggs and dairy produce.

Verbal Communication that uses words.

Voluntary organisations These are non-profit-making organisations, sometimes registered as charities, which provide services to bridge gaps in statutory provision, sometimes free of charge.

Wealth The value of the property owned by a person. Wealth includes the value of houses, cars, savings and any other personal possessions.

White Paper A government document setting out its proposals for the provision of services.

Answers to tests

Unit 1

Answers to the 'Think it over' features in this Unit follow the answers to the Unit 1 Test.

1   Statutory services.

2   Any three of the following: planning services within its area; assessing primary health care needs; developing services within its area; commissioning primary care; arranging community services; managing community services; monitoring the quality of services; providing information for the public; registering and dealing with complaints.

3   **b**.

4   Three examples would be a nursery school, a crèche and a playgoup.

5   Direct is used to describe those jobs where the worker has face-to-face contact with the client. Indirect is used to describe those jobs where the worker supports those who come into face-to-face contact with the clients but where the workers may not come into contact with the clients him or herself.

6   Three skills might include: communication skills (verbal and written); the ability to take in large amounts of information and to be able to analyse; the ability to work flexibly – both alone and in teams.

7   0–8 years.

8   Values are basic principles that guide practice in care work. Values help care workers to protect vulnerable individuals.

9   Practical ways of valuing diversity include: using listening skills to build an understanding; treating everyone as individuals and offering choices; finding ways to show respect and value for individuals; respecting the rights of others; avoiding making assumptions about people; following policies on equal opportunities.

10 Rights and responsibilities include: freedom from discrimination; a right to be independent; a right to make choices; a right to receive respect and dignity; a right to safety and security; a right to confidentiality.

11 Codes of practice and charters are needed to provide a definition of good quality care that can be measured.

12 Communication skills are used to understand the needs of others, make relationships, show respect and value for others and meet emotional and social needs.

13 Non-verbal communication is communicating without using words. Non-verbal communication includes body language and tone and volume of voice.

14 Listening is an active process, where your own non-verbal communication and conversation skills show the other person that you have understood what they are saying. Listening forms part of the communication syle. Hearing just means that you have received the sounds that another person makes. Listening is about understanding.

Answers to Think it over questions on pages 17 and 48

Page 17
The organisation which uses this symbol is ChildLine, a voluntary organisation which provides a free national helpline for children and young people in trouble or danger. It was founded by Esther Rantzen in October 1986.

Page 48, Safety hazards in the kitchen

Crockery is left unwashed, with particles of decaying food around.

Electrical safety – the kettle lead is near water, creating a risk of electric shock. The electrical point might be overloaded with too many connections. The toaster is too near the sink and water supply.

Fresh food is left uncovered – flies can land on it and spread micro-organisms from the decaying food in the sink and bin. Micro-organisms from the air can also contaminate the food.

Bleach can be hazardous – it should not be stored near food. Here the lid is off and there is a risk of spillage or even food contamination.

Food preparation surfaces have not been cleaned, allowing micro-organisms to build up and transfer to fresh food.

Knives are not stored in a safe way.

Decaying food is left in a broken pedal bin, encouraging flies and the spread of micro-organisms.

Fresh food is placed near decaying food, encouraging the spread of micro-organisms.

The dishcloth is contaminated with micro-organisms from the (dirty) floor area – separate floor and dishcloths should be used.

The dirty floor might create a hazard of slipping and falling, as well as encouraging the spread of micro-organisms.

The mop and bucket might be tripped over.

Unit 2

1   a.
2   a and b.
3   c.
4   d.
5   b.
6   c.
7   d.
8   b and d.
9   a.
10   c.
11   d.
12   Carbohydrates; fat and protein (in the correct proportions) to provide energy, growth and repair; sufficient vitamins, mineral salts, water and fibre to sustain a healthy lifestyle.
13   Any three of the following. Eat less salt; more fibre; less fat; more vitamins and mineral salts; more fresh fruit and vegetables.
14   Fibre stimulates bowel movement; prevents constipation; gives us a feeling of fullness; prevents bowel disorders.
15   Proteins for growth and repair, fats and carbohydrates for energy.
16   We need energy to manufacture cells when we are growing. Adolescents are growing rapidly, old people are not.
17   People in professional classes (1.1, 1.2, 2) may consume diets rich in animal fats and may be overweight. They may take less exercise due to pressure of work. Stress at work is likely to be great, with no time for stress management techniques. All the above can combine to cause heart attacks and strokes. This group of people may abuse alcohol in the form of wine and spirits.
18   To provide fibre, vitamins and mineral salts.
19   Health education units, doctors' surgeries, dentists' surgeries, health centres, etc.
20   Any four of the following: addiction; force of habit; lack of motivation; low self-esteem; too busy; lack of child care; low income.

Unit 3

Scenario one

1   Any one of the following. *Physically*: growth, reflexes, development of muscle control; *intellectually*: muscle control; babbling; learning how physical objects work; *emotionally*: attachment to carer (bonding), guided by carer's behaviour; *socially*: recognise carer, respond to carer.

2   Sitting, crawling, bear-walking, walking alone, toilet training.

3   Spend time playing with Anil. Encourage social and language development through talk and interaction. Provide good-quality toys and activities that will encourage his intellectual development.

4   Anil may be able to bond or build an emotional attachment with the people who provide attention. Anil may feel safe when familiar people are around him.

5   Any one of the following: in her grammatical use of language; a much larger vocabulary; her play will imitate social behaviour; her muscle co-ordination skills will be more developed (such as climbing, running and jumping).

6   The parents spend less time with Anil. This may influence Anil's intellectual development – less practice with talking, less encouragement with play. If his parents became emotionally withdrawn, this may upset Anil's attachment to them – he may feel less emotionally secure.

7   Any three of the following: impairments of hearing and vision; problems with her heart, breathing and circulation; less efficient muscle strength; the onset of arthritis; slower reactions; risk of brittle bones; her kidneys and liver may be less efficient. (*Note*: dementia, loss of memory or senility are incorrect answers – these problems only happen to a minority of older people.)

8   Family and friends provide relationships. Relationships prevent social isolation and protect people from stress. Relationships may create a positive sense of 'self-esteem' or 'self-worth'. Relationships may create a sense of belonging and they meet social and emotional needs. Living with the family may help the grandmother maintain a positive self-concept.

9   Praise will encourage the development of a positive self-concept and of positive self-esteem.

10 Gender role.

11 Any three of the following: secure attachments in infancy; friendships; family relationships; positive feedback from other people; success with activities or with school work or sports; positive opportunities and environment; belonging to a clear culture shared by his family and friends; being popular.

12 Going with his family to worship at the local temple; mixing with other children at school.

Scenario two

13 Any four of the following: parents stressed by money worries; overcrowding; poor diet; more hazardous housing; fewer resources to help with school work; less chance of keeping up with the latest styles of clothing; low expectations of success in life; pollution; noise; petty crime.

14 There are no eggs left in the woman's ovaries.

15 Any two of the following: onset of menstruation; increased fat deposited under her skin; pubic and under-arm hair growth; enlargement of her breasts.

16 It will affect her self-concept because it will have a positive effect on her self-esteem and self-worth: she may feel more independent, more adult, may have a higher status among her friends and may feel more in control of life.

17 Any two of the following: understanding herself as a member of a partnership or couple; being independent; being responsible for the home.

18 Failing eyesight, particularly at night; bones may have become more brittle; their sense of balance may be impaired; their sensitivity to heat, cold and pain could all be reduced; their smell and hearing could be impaired.

19 Any one of the following. *Physical*: enough sleep and rest; coping with stress and pressure; *intellectual*: learning about new people, new tasks, new routines; learning how to cope with new activities; *emotional*: self-esteem needs – the need to feel competent, the need to keep a positive self-concept; the need for positive feedback from others; *social*: the need to belong, fit in; the need for respect; the need for inclusion in social activity.

20 Any three of the following: denial, anger, resistance to change, guilt, withdrawal, trying out new ways of coping.

Suggestions for further reading and useful websites

Books

Body fitness and exercise, M. Rosser (Hodder & Stoughton, 1995).

A handbook for care assistants, S. Benson (Care Concern, 1995).

Human life, D. G. McKean (John Murray, 1988).

Human biology and health studies, Martin Rowland (Nelson, 1996).

Investigating health, welfare and poverty, P. Trowler (Unwin Hyman, 1989).

Website addresses

www.active.org.uk An interactive website which helps you to analyse how much exercise you are getting, and comes up with ideas for how you can become more active.

www.avert.org.uk AIDS Education and Research Trust – information and education about HIV issues.

www.lifesaver.co.uk Offers support and motivation to help people stop smoking

www.lovelife.hea.org.uk Sexual health website for young people.

www.quick.org.uk How to check whether you can trust the information you find on the Internet.

www.thinkfast.co.uk Helpful advice on how to make healthy choices when eating fast food.

www.trashed.co.uk Website offering information about drugs and their effects.

www.wrecked.co.uk Facts about the effects of alcohol and alcohol abuse.

The page numbers in brackets refer to Fast Facts.